Nursing Home Nightmares

Nursing Home Nightmares

America's Disgrace

A True Story of Abuse, Neglect And Corporate Greed

Dr. Glenn Mollette

Milo House Press
New York, New York

Cover by Ronda Hodge

Printed in the United States of America

In memory of
those neglected until they died
in
American Nursing Homes

Table of Contents

1

Thinking About A Nursing Home

Hitting bottom comes in different ways to different people. To some, it's spending their last dollar, while to others, it is hearing the news, *it's cancer and you only have six months to live.* To some, it's when their spouse of twenty years says, *I don't love you anymore and I'm filing for divorce.* To others, it is when they receive heart-wrenching news from a policeman who comes to their door and says, *I'm so sorry but your child has been killed.* I think the worst few moments of my life was when I awakened from sleep at 10:00 Saturday night, October 21, 2000 and realized Karen was in serious trouble.

For several weeks Karen had been going into deep sleep. She would sleep for two or three hours and it was difficult to wake her. The visiting nurses from St. Martha's Hospital would question why she was sleeping so much. Later I would learn that the girl I had hired part-time to help out with Karen, was making phone calls to St. Martha's and Social Services saying that she suspected I was giving Karen too much medicine and that was causing her to go into such deep sleeps. The truth of the matter was that Karen was on high dosages of several different medications that she received two and three times a day

Continuation of Silent Struggle.
Desires on getting up home
nursing

2   Dr. Glenn Mollette

depending on the medicine, and there was no way she could keep from sleeping a lot—and deeply.

By 8:00 Saturday night I had laid down in bed to study some sermon notes for the next Sunday morning. Karen had a comfortable motorized wheelchair and was deeply asleep. By ten o'clock I was awakened by what sounded like heavy snoring coming from Karen. But as I got up and tried to wake her for bed, it wasn't going to happen. She was totally unconscious. Calling 911, I described to them that Karen needed help. When they arrived and pulled back the blanket that was on top of her, several different pills were found spilled over her lap. It was an obvious suicide effort. The paramedics moved quickly securing Karen in their medical van and asked me to gather up all of Karen's medications for them to take to the hospital so they would know how to treat her.

It became a long night that turned into a long weekend and then a long week. The emergency room nurses would pump Karen's stomach and also inject her stomach with a substance they called charcoal that would absorb some of the medication that had not made it into her blood stream. She would then be placed on a ventilator and moved to the Intensive Care Unit of the hospital where she would lay unconscious for almost three days. Finally on the third day there was some eye movement and it seemed Karen was coming back to life.

This was the one place she had asked me never to bring her. "Glenn, don't ever take me back to the hospital. I don't ever want to be in the ICU unit on a respirator. Please just let me die the next time you find me unconscious or in trouble." I felt awful. I knew Karen would awaken enough to realize where she was and deplore the ventilator and all the tubes running in and out of her body.

As she opened her eyes all I knew to say was, "I hate that you are here. But I had no choice. I couldn't sit and watch you die. I love you and need you too much for you to leave us." Karen was unable to respond while on the ventilator but I knew that her mood and feelings of depression had to be at an all time low.

When her health stabilized enough to remove the breathing tube and Karen was able to whisper enough to get out a few words, the first she said to me were, "Why didn't you let me go?"

"I couldn't let you. I love you and we need you. You don't realize what a blessing you are to us. Plus I couldn't have lived with myself if I had just sat there and watched you die."

Karen would soon be strong enough to move to a room out of the Intensive Care Unit of the hospital but then what? I was beginning to be faced with a question that was becoming increasingly louder, *how am I going to care for Karen?* Here is someone I loved and she as a person meant everything to us as a family. But now it was becoming increasingly difficult to care for her at home. We had home health care, a hired helper and ladies from the church that came by to help out but it seemed like it still wasn't enough. Plus if Karen came home and got her hands on too much medication and overdosed, then Social Services would be on my back suspecting me of being a culprit in trying to harm Karen. The whole scenario of living under such pressure prompted me to consider nursing homes. The very thought of putting Karen into a nursing home was unnerving and scary. I knew this was the last place Karen wanted to be. Her entire hope in ending her life was that she might avoid laying in a nursing home bed as a total invalid unable to feed or do anything for herself. I now saw that fear unfolding, as a potential reality and I hated it for her and for all of us.

Karen was diagnosed with multiple sclerosis in February 1990 by an ophthalmologist in East Kentucky. She was having a little trouble with her vision and went for a routine eye examine. He gave her his diagnosis of her vision trouble. "Karen, you have multiple sclerosis." It was an unbelievable diagnosis that we could hardly believe and fought with every ounce of our beings for twelve years. We saw doctors all over the United States—even going to Mayo Clinic in Rochester,

Minnesota. Mayo Clinic by the way was off in their diagnosis. Their report to Karen was that she had a very *mild* case of multiple sclerosis and would likely never be bothered with it. They were wrong.

Karen was progressive with her disease, going from tingling in her legs and feet to dragging her right leg because of the numbness. From there she progressed to a debilitation that would put her permanently in a wheelchair and even take away her ability to feed herself, touch her face or even allow her to turn herself over in bed. Over a twelve year period of time I watched this beautiful, healthy woman go from teaching school in the public school system and playing a grand piano, to having every personal need she had met at my hands and the hands of nurses and aides. Multiple sclerosis is an insidious disease.

For the most part of Karen's illness we had been able to cope at home. She managed on her walker. She could get around the house and in her wheelchair. Even when I had to literally pick her up and place her on the toilet seat of the bathroom, it was difficult but manageable.

When I have looked back at Karen's digressing health I would often look at those times when I would have to help her dress and think, *this is about as bad as it can get.* I would learn that it can get worse and probably will with a disease such as multiple sclerosis. It did continue to get worse for Karen; and when it did, I would remember back to the six months prior and think, *it would be easier if we could just go back to that time period when she was able to brush her own teeth or hold her own drink.*

My mother is currently battling Alzheimer's. At this writing she is still able to walk a little and feed herself. Most likely by the time this book is in print, her ability to walk and feed herself may be over. I have told my father and sisters who care for her, "Enjoy the present because in six months you will look back to this time and think, *I wish we could go back to that time frame and have her as she was then.*" It's only when a person becomes much worse that we can appreciate the little bit of health they had previously.

I began to inquire on the hospital floor about who to talk to about help with finding an appropriate nursing care facility. I didn't have the first clue as to who to talk to and how to go about finding a nursing home. After all, this was something that 75 year-old people did. Forty-five-year-old people don't have to inquire about nursing homes. Karen was only 47 at the time. How many 47-year-old men or women are in nursing homes? I would later find out there are several. However, the bulk of nursing home residents are well into their senior years above sixty-five-years-old and much older.

At our age we were faced with raising two teenage boys and thinking about high school, college and daily life. The last thing any American family would be considering in their middle age years is nursing home care. When disease strikes, it takes away most all normalcy.

My thought at the time was that maybe if we could find a place where Karen could receive good medical care and physical therapy that it would be more healthy for her than bringing her home where medical care was relegated to visiting home health care and phone calls to the doctor's office. Physical therapy on her declining physical movements was of the utmost necessity. Stretching her legs—that now wanted to draw up against her bottom and were very nonflexible—was important to Karen being able to rest at night.

Surely there would be a place in the Evansvelle, Indiana area that had a suitable nursing care facility that could give my wife the kind of medical care she deserved, I thought.

Unfortunately I was thinking like most any other American. I don't know how other countries overall handle their sick and elderly. I know that as a country we are blessed in so many ways in comparison to much of the world. Elderly and sick people in many third world countries would feel as if they had died and gone to heaven if they had a room to sleep in such as our nursing home residents have in America. In countries where people literally fight their diseases in streets and ravines and die in open public places they would surely feel an American nursing home would be a place of paradise. But let's not linger on this point long. America is not a third world country. America is the richest country in the world. We have in contrast to the rest of the world very rich and comfortable lives. We are blessed.

We also have become accustomed to doing about whatever we want without any encumbrances. We have freedom. We have so much freedom that we have grown accustomed to not being bogged down by commitments such as family. The divorce rate is now at fifty percent in many states and will likely increase unless there is a sweeping change in attitude in this country. We are very understanding of divorce and social change in our country. If a man or woman doesn't want to stay married they divorce. It's not always simple. If there is money involved it really becomes complicated. When children are involved it's a serious matter of mediation, especially if both spouses want custody. Yet, regardless of the consequences, people get married and people divorce for different reasons. This is a fact of our society and of course much of the world.

It seems we have accepted the idea that it is easier to just go our separate ways than to work things out. And truthfully, there are some marriages and relationships that cannot be resolved, and sadly divorce seems to be the only way. I believe with God all things are possible. I do feel that many marriages could have been saved if both people had looked to God for help and sought professional counseling. Today, many people are quick to dissolve a relationship and move on. We like to *move on* and get on with life.

Going to counseling, seeking God's help means trying and making an effort that requires time, work, and patience. Unfortunately, too many today are not interested in anything that requires a lot of time or effort when it comes to relationships.

Our sick loved ones are relationships that require time, patience and effort. This is where the rub comes in. We've developed a mentality that says *we don't have the time*. We say, *we don't have the time to take care of Dad, Mom, Husband, Wife or child. They require so much attention. They require help with dressing, eating, bathing and I just can't do it for them*. Truthfully, it often reaches a point where we can't. And when we can't . . . we can't.

Unfortunately we are often quick on the draw. We end a marriage because we've had a few bad days in the relationship. We are ready to turn a child over to foster care because they have become unmanageable and we quip, *we don't have the time or the ability to handle our unmanageable child*. This attitude therefore is one that fully comes into play when we have to deal with a sick family member. We unload ourselves of encumbering relationships and move on. This is not an easy thought for us. But it's the truth of our society we live in.

Nursing homes exist so that we can unload ourselves of a family relationship and move on with our lives. Think about it this way. Nursing homes exist so that our children can unload themselves of having to put up with us and move on with their carefree lives. Consider it this way. Nursing homes exist so that your spouse has a place to unload you and go on with his/her daily golf games, card outings and footloose life so that he/she will not have to be bothered changing your underpants, giving you a bath or being concerned about your welfare. Harsh statements? No. . . . *Realities.*

Reality and truth are always harsher than imagination and fiction. When Karen was in the hospital struggling to regain her life, I thought only what came naturally to people most everywhere—nursing home. *Surely, a good nursing home is the answer. It will be a place where caring, loving, helpful people will see to it that Karen will be properly fed, bathed, clothed, given physical therapy and be taken care of medically. I continued to think she would be better cared for in a nursing home facility. There will be lots of good trained nurses, caring aides, dieticians and helpful administrative people in charge of seeing to Karen's care and best interests.*

I have never been more wrong in all my life. What I believed would be helpful and a blessing to my wife, became a six-month nightmare that almost cost us Karen's very life.

I have visited nursing homes. I have conducted worship services in nursing homes as a minister. I have heard people talk negatively about nursing homes. I had some of my own fears I had gathered about nursing homes. Most of those fears have been seeing people sit listlessly in the halls or walking by nursing home rooms that reeked of urine. But all that I ever thought about nursing homes pales in comparison to the reality, which is far worse than I ever imagined or feared.

How have we gotten to such a state of life that we put away the people that we love the very most in places where they will experience the very worst of life? We have allowed ourselves to become such a mobile, busy, overworked, overstressed society that seeing a relative through to the very end has become almost impossible. Caring for somebody in our home with the help of other family members pitching in to relieve us is almost totally voided from our way of thinking. We don't think that way because we know in most cases the other family members have their lives and they don't have the time to help with the sick wife, husband, mom or aunt Bessie.

And when the time comes, all those same people will be too busy to give an iota about you.

When health and life change for the worst, we too quickly think of nursing homes as a remedy for the situation. Sadly, most people don't know what they are getting themselves into, until it's too late.

2

Finding A Nursing Home

After Karen slowly regained total consciousness and began to breathe on her own I was asked by the hospital social worker, "What are your plans for Karen?" I would later hear this question a thousand times.

"My plans?"

"Yes," she replied, "What are you going to do with Karen?"

Doesn't the question sound strange to you? It did to me. Here is an intelligent human life. She has battled a horrible disease for over 12 years and her body is beginning to be ravaged by its relentless progression. Yet, I am in the position of responding, "I have plans for her?" This was new and uncharted territory for me. As the unit social worker for the hospital, she wanted to be helpful so she gave me her card and said I could call anytime. The next day I was in her office asking, "What are our options?" I said, *our options* because this was a decision that had to be the best for Karen as well as our family.

I found out that day most of what I had already guessed. If Karen came home, we were looking at home health care, which is what we already had been using. But home health care was coming to our home only an hour a day. The nurse came and took the vital signs. An aide would come three times a week to give Karen a bath. When the aide was showing up, most of the time they needed me to sit Karen on her bath bench. If I had to be home to sit Karen on the bath bench then it was just as easy to give her the bath. So, why did I need the aide? It was actually an encumbrance on my time since I had to adjust my schedule to accommodate the aide's schedule.

The idea of taking Karen home to the scenario of limited home health care was unnerving. It would be tough. Plus with Karen's declining motor abilities she needed physical therapy more and more. Even if she couldn't walk, her legs still needed manipulated to keep them flexible and give her some relief from having them in a fetal position most of the time.

I also found out from the social worker that there were a lot of nursing homes in our area of Evansvelle and Southern, Indiana. She gave me an entire 8x11 sheet of paper with names and phone numbers of nursing homes on the front and back.

"These nursing homes all have different amounts they charge for their services. Take a look and see what you think is best for your family."

Staring briefly at the sheet of paper I began to see $4,200 a month and $4,500 a month and other prices.

"Medicare will pay for so many days. Talk to the admissions counselor at the place of your choice. They will help you with your questions concerning financial arrangements."

Looking at a blank list of nursing homes was daunting. I immediately spotted a couple of homes in our area where I had visited people as a minister. When I thought of the names of those homes I immediately recalled the stench of urine and unhappy people sitting in the hallways waiting for someone to do something for them or even look their way with just a moment of attention. *Could I emotionally bear to have my wife sitting in one of these places that I had already found totally repulsive?* I didn't see how I could do it.

I thanked the social worker and went back to look at Karen in her hospital bed. She was resting better and was off the respirator.

The next day I began dropping by nursing homes. I visited the ones closest to home. I knew some of the people who worked in them and they were gracious to show me around. However, what could they show me? All they could show me was a room with two beds in it. They could take me down the hallway where lonely people sat. They could take me to a dining hall where people looked almost comatose as aides spoon-fed them. Or, they were able to show me a recreation area where someone was up singing, trying to exhort the handful of people sitting in the recreation hall to join in singing. They didn't look too enthusiastic. So, these little tours were supposed to help me make a decision about placing my wife into their care? About the only thing a nursing home tour will help you decide is what an awful step you are about to make with a loved one by placing them into such a facility.

One nursing home I visited raved about the good food they had. "We have a Master Chef in our kitchen," the admissions counselor beamed. She didn't tell me the home had a pending case against them because one of the residents in the home had murdered another resident. A case still yet unresolved. In another facility the admissions counselor promoted the spaciousness of the rooms. Yet, as I went from nursing home to nursing home I found the tours were short and the information given about the facility was brief.

Why? What can a nursing home admissions counselor say? Showing a potential family a nursing home is not like a realtor showing off a house. It's a facility, but a very limited one. There are no open kitchens, great rooms or luxurious baths to show off. It's simply a room with two beds unless you are very wealthy and can afford a private room, which is seldom found in most nursing homes.

After a couple of days of searching I knew I had to make a decision about a home and begin the admissions process. The first one I decided on, took my application for Karen and then the next day called and

12   Dr. Glenn Mollette

my experience was a Corer

turned us down. The reason . . . "Mr. Mollette, your wife needs acute care and we can't handle acute care patients here. We are so very sorry." I was sorry, too. At least they were honest. If a nursing home cannot handle somebody, then they should say upfront—which is what this particular home did. Besides we were looking for a lot of help with Karen. We needed some place that would try to help her besides feed her and keep her clean—which are very, very important. I would later realize how vitally important. Yet, we were looking for medical support and physical therapy as well as making sure that Karen was kept comfortable.

A couple of days later a young nurse from my church would tell me about a place where she had begun working. "I hear you are looking for a nursing home? I've started working at a new place and they seem to really care. You might check us out." I followed her lead and the next day was touring the Anglican River Nursing Home.

The building was less than two years old and still had a new fresh look to it. The furniture was still in good shape and there was a respectable appearance to it. This was refreshing in comparison to the other nursing homes I had toured. The admissions counselor was very courteous and helpful. She gave me a tour and told me, "We are full to capacity. But, if you want to be on the waiting list I'll call you when something comes open."

When something comes open? How long would this take?

"We could have an opening any day," she replied.

At the time it didn't dawn on me what she meant. Later after Karen had been admitted for a month or so, she would tell me about seeing the funeral home hearse pull in and another black bag carried out of the nursing home. "The beds here empty pretty fast," she would say.

When the admissions counselor was talking to me about beds becoming available, it didn't dawn on me how they were becoming empty. It wasn't because people were getting well and going home.

One of my big concerns was the kind of medical care and physical therapy Karen would receive. I was told of the physician's care she would receive. I was informed about the very adequate nursing staff and then given a tour of the physical therapy department. I was sold. Surely this was the very place I was looking for.

I left Anglican River being told that I would be called as soon as a bed became available. As I drove out of the parking lot I was encouraged again as I saw the sign that read, "Anglican River Health and Rehabilitation." Surely this would be a place where Karen could receive some help and could be cared for in a very adequate way.

Unfortunately when I look back on the entire admissions process I am appalled. There was no information given to me on what I could expect from Anglican River Nursing Home. I was told they had good nurses and good aides and they had physical therapy. The rooms were clean and the placed smelled okay. I was introduced to no one else. I was not introduced to the administrator. I was not introduced to the head of nursing, the social worker for the home or any of the nurses or staff. I wasn't introduced to any of the patients. I was given the ten-minute tour; my application was taken; and then I was assured I would be called if something became available. And of course the major part of the admissions time was spent talking about finances. My wife was in the hospital and we had Medicare. Medicare would cover the costs of the nursing home stay for a brief time period until something permanently could be worked out. The admissions counselor was doing her job. She was courteous.

Nursing homes are for profit. They are by and large big money makers for corporations that see first and foremost the bottom line. They do not see the care of the patients first and foremost. They see profit first. The idea for them is to house, feed and care for somebody for the lowest amount of money possible so that they can put the largest amount of money possible into their pockets. The care of our loved ones is sacrificed in order for nursing home owners to pocket huge amounts of cash. Do these owners care that people in their nursing homes get huge bed sores and staph infections, lay awake all night with fevers, go un-bathed and sometimes are abused verbally and physically? No. They are big money makers. How many nursing homes have you seen shut down in your community? You may see a restaurant close because of bad food or bad service. Do you ever see a nursing home close on account of bad food or bad service? No. Nursing homes are allowed to feed the residents bad food, render horrendous service and stay open 24 hours a day—mostly all paid for by the tax dollars of the American people. It is an American disgrace. Why do we put up with it? We don't put up with bad service from any other entity in our nation. We won't even tip a bad waiter at a restaurant. We won't go back to a mechanic who is incapable of properly servicing the car. We scold at our dry cleaners if they mess up a skirt or suit. Why . . . in the world do we put up with such garbage when it comes to people!?! And these are not just people but they are our family members. These people are husbands, wives, mothers, fathers or grandparents. They are blood relatives who use to in many instances, help and care for us and now we have allowed them to go into places where the food is lousy, the rooms are smelly and the care often isn't even kind and caring. A doctor may see the loved one whenever he gets around to it . . . sometime, when he is doing nothing else. We allow our dearest loved ones to be in places where they go for hours with fevers, days with viruses and even months with infections. Dear God . . . forgive us!

Absolutely no admission's counseling was given to me at Anglican River. Nothing was told to me about what they would be doing to help Karen. Nothing was discussed as to what was expected of our family or me. I was never told what I could do as the husband of my wife. Nothing from the administration or admissions process clued me in as to any perimeters that the nursing home administration had for family members. Because of my wife's lingering fever I bought a bottle of

Advil and gave her some at night so she could sleep. This was because she couldn't get the third shift nurse to give her any. She would lay awake all night burning up from fever . . . calling out for someone to help her. The administration of the nursing home gave me a royal hard time for giving my wife some Advil. Yet, there was no upfront meeting with the administration to discuss that it would be inappropriate for me to try to help my sick wife who was literally burning up with fever due to their negligence. Inappropriate? Yes, to them. I, giving my wife Advil because she was burning up with fever, was offensive to them. It was offensive to Karen and I, too. After begging and begging for help day after day with this fever for several months it grew increasingly offensive. A simple Tylenol or Advil at night calmed the fever and enabled her to rest. Imagine the panic this woman felt when she thought she was not going to receive anything to help.

Looking back, it shouldn't have taken a rocket scientist to figure out something was causing the fever. *Where were the nursing home medical personnel? Why hadn't the doctor investigated the fever? Why would they allow her to go week after week with fever simply treating it with Tylenol and no other antibiotics? Why was no medical research done to find out what was causing it?* I will come back to this later.

Unfortunately I fear this is a scenario being played out in nursing homes all over America. People are being neglected. We are allowing them to be warehoused until such time that they can be buried and totally out of the way. That's not how we want to think about it. We want to think that we are doing what is best for our family member. I think in many cases we have the best intentions that the nursing home facility will be a comfortable and happy place for our parent or spouse. This is what we talk ourselves into believing. Keep dreaming. It is truly your wildest imagination at work.

Think about yourself. Is a nursing home where you want to spend the last three years of your life? How about the last six months? How about your last day? Is a nursing home where you want to breath your last breath? Do you want to be some place where your last meal was bad, your last breath stank, the last face you saw didn't give a dang about how you felt, the last great thing that somebody did for you was give you a bath and probably only a half of a one at that? No! We don't want this for ourselves. Why do we allow it for somebody we love?

I grant us a little mercy here. We do it because we run out of physical and emotional fuel of being able to do it. When the whole load of caring for someone falls on the shoulders of one or even two people it becomes a task that is almost impossible. And therefore we turn to the nursing home places of America because we feel hopeless and helpless. And these places for many years now in our country have stood with their doors wide opened preying upon worn out families and sole caregivers.

The average nursing home doesn't even promise to care for your loved one. When you interview a nursing home counselor, listen to see if any promises are made to care for your family member. They show you the room and tell you how much will be billed to Medicare and Medicaid. They will answer questions when you ask them. I'm writing this book to tell you to ask questions. Make out your list of questions and ask them. However, I want to warn you if the nursing home administration thinks you are going to be any kind of nuisance at all they will decline your admissions request. Nursing homes don't want to be bothered with family members asking questions and snooping to see if the loved one is being properly cared for. They want patients whose family members come for about thirty minutes once a week and then are not around any other time. This way they can let the loved one sit in his/her bowel movement for hours and develop bedsores that are never seen by the family member. Any family around the nursing home asking questions and giving any kind of suggestions to the nursing staff means extra work that most nursing staffs are not able to physically handle.

When you visit a nursing home and interview with them about what to expect, get all the answers. Meet with the admissions counselor. Ask to meet the administrator. Ask to talk to the head of nursing. Ask to talk to the social worker. Ask to meet the nurses who work in the section of the nursing home where your loved one will be. Furthermore, ask for names of references. Ask if you may talk to any families who have loved ones in the nursing home. Chances are they will have to get their permission to give you their names. But they will find happy people for you to talk to. Go ahead and talk to these people because helpful information will come out in the conversation. They may have names of other people who have family members in the nursing home. Obtain the names through them and contact these people. Be prepared to ask questions about how their loved one is being treated.

Ask how they feel they are being treated as a visiting family member. After all, the nursing home journey is not just about the resident. It's about the whole family who weekly or daily visits the loved one. If the nursing home is not congenial about your visits and interest in the loved one, then this is a sure warning to be wary of such a place.

The nursing home will become the second home for the family member who visit's the loved one every day. In my case I went every day for an hour. Some days I was there twice for more than an hour. How the visiting family is treated is important since this becomes like a second home to the resident's family.

When you have asked all the questions you can from everybody at the nursing home and people who know anything about it, then before you make any decisions, check out the following website information on the Internet: www.medicare.gov./ It will list every nursing home in your county and their ratings. It reveals how they have fared inspections and how they compare with other nursing homes. After taking Karen out of Anglican River I heard about this website and found that Anglican River while it has a clean building, has one of the poorest ratings of any nursing home in our area.

Make sure you receive upfront information about any care that you cannot give to the loved one. Are you allowed to help them dress? Are you allowed to take them for lunch? Are you allowed to help them turn over in bed? Are you allowed to put lip balm on their lips? Are you allowed to put lotion on their bodies? Are you allowed to check them for bedsores or any beginnings of bedsores? Are you allowed to put any kind of salve or ointment on any skin discolorations? Are you allowed to bring in food? Are you allowed to take them to the doctor? Is there any time you are not allowed to visit? If so, what are these hours and why?

Ask also the name of county ombudsman. The nursing home admissions counselor should provide you with this name. This person is the individual who is supposed to be on the side of the family and patient in the nursing home. They are supposed to be able to tell you the ins and outs of any nursing home in their respective county. They should be able to alert you to any negative reports on any nursing home under their local jurisdiction. Also their role is to help you in rectifying or reconciling any problem you are having with your respective nursing home. I never knew such a person existed until about two weeks before I took Karen out of Anglican River and brought her back home. No one from the administrator, the social worker, the head of nursing or admissions counselor told me that such a person existed.

Why wouldn't they? Nursing home administrators don't often tell about the local ombudsman because they don't want to be bothered with any entity on their backs about how they are not doing their jobs. It is one of their ways of keeping the family members of loved ones as far out of the nursing home administration's hair as possible.

One of the saddest episodes of my wife's tenure with Anglican River was when after five months, Casey, the administrator, and I sat in her office. We had just been through a very heated day of meetings, which I will describe later. She hung her head and said, "Glenn, we should have had this meeting at the very beginning. We could have saved ourselves all of this." I have wished many times with all that Anglican River did to my wife and put me through that some kind of upfront meeting to provide information and direction could have taken place. But it didn't happen and so many families every day in America are blindly going through the motions of searching out nursing care facilities and they are leaving their loved one in nursing homes without a clue as to what to expect . . . unknowing the reputation of the nursing home. Often it is like a wilderness experience where the family finds out one mountain and valley at a time what the nursing home life is all about. Or it's like a puzzle where daily you find a new piece of information about the nursing home. The only thing about finally putting the entire puzzle together is that when you put the last piece in place—your loved one is dead.

3

Transporting Karen To The Nursing Home

Karen was in St. Martha's Hospital for two weeks recuperating from her overdose of medication but the day was quickly approaching for her dismissal.

Arrangements had been made for a bed at Anglican River.

"Karen we are moving you to a place that offers rehabilitation," I said.

"Where is this?" she asked.

"The side of town we live on has a facility that offers rehabilitation. It will give you the opportunity to have some professional people work with your arms and legs and hopefully you will regain some of the use of them that you have lost."

Karen was willing to try.

I viewed Anglican River as a facility that had a physical therapy department and would be an environment where Karen could be physically helped. The admissions counselor had been friendly and the environment looked fine. Of course this was only the surface that I saw.

I heard a friend say once, "You really don't know someone until you are married."

You don't nursing homes either until you or someone you care about has actually lived in one for a couple of months.

The social worker at our hospital would coordinate with Anglican River Karen's release from the hospital and her delivery to the nursing home. It was an awful day for both of us. For several months I had been wondering if I would have to put Karen into a nursing home facility. Just the thought of her being a resident in one was emotionally painful to me. There had been a couple of times that Karen and I had breached the subject. It was not a place where Karen wanted to go. It was not a place where I wanted to take her.

But Anglican River seemed a little different. It was newer, brighter and cleaner. It wasn't that far from home so I would be able to easily check on Karen a couple of times a day. After she was admitted I would often go twice a day and spend as much as an hour or more each visit. During most of her stay at the facility I would take her out for lunch once or twice a week. I would pick her up and take her to our home for several hours so she could have a break from the nursing home environment.

I checked on Karen the morning she was to be released from St. Martha's. The transportation vehicle was scheduled to arrive sometime in the morning. The kind of vehicle was one that enables a person in a wheelchair to be loaded into the side of the van with the assistance of a hydraulic lift.

I was daily running in ten different directions. While I was trying to be an attentive and caring husband for Karen, I also was trying to be a pastor to a growing and changing suburban church. There were always other members who were in the hospital, or who wanted an appointment with the pastor or there were administrative details to attend to along with a couple of sermons to write every week. Pastors technically work 24 hours a day. While they may not be sitting in a church office all the time, pastors/ministers are always at work. Wherever they go in town, people see them as being on duty. While I normally dress casually I am always approached wherever I am in the community, and eventually church in some capacity is a topic.

Along with our church, Karen and I have two teenage boys. Karen's being sick, and in and out of the hospital, placed me in the role of not only being a caregiver to Karen but also that of a single parent. Sometimes I hear single parents moan about how hard it is for them. At least they only have their children to care for. What if they had to care for their ex-spouse and wait on the ex off and on 24 hours a day? It would drive most any single parent nuts.

Karen and I have had a strong and growing love throughout the duration of her multiple sclerosis illness. Caring for her in a care giving role has changed my life and given me a dimension of comprehension about life that most people do not gain until their senior years. This has enabled me to relate to people in ways I never knew existed before.

The vehicle came and picked Karen up while I was out. I would later call the nurses to see what the *arrangements* for the transportation vehicle would be. I was told, "They've already come and gone."

"You mean they've already picked Karen up?"

"Yes, she's gone."

I knew Karen would be apprehensive about being transported to a new facility.

I called Anglican River and was told by the nurse on her wing, "Your wife is here. She is in her room. I think she's upset."

I could only imagine. I began to think about the transportation people taking Karen into that nursing care facility. I knew she would likely be taken by a lot of elderly people in the hallways. It would have to be distressing to her. To make everything horribly worse, the nursing home personnel began talking to Karen about this being her new home.

"New Home?" she asked. "I am not here to live. I am here to get better."

What a distressing thought to any human being who has lived in his/her own home for many years to suddenly be taken to a place where there is a half bed, a night stand, and a dresser that you share with a roommate, and then to be told, "Welcome to your new home." Wow, what a stimulating greeting for anyone to think that all of your life, hard work and efforts have come down to this tiny little space.

Sadly it is true that our lives do come down to a tiny little room that we share with another sick or elderly person in most cases. Many people spend their last few days drawing their last few breaths of air in such strange surroundings being cared for by nursing home staff who are strangers and who are very overworked and very underpaid. This means they are normally frustrated people who are trying to do the right things such as be nice and considerate but they are asked to do too much in their roles as nurses or aides. There will be more about this later.

By the time I arrived at Anglican River, they already had Karen relegated to her gown and in bed. When she looked up at me her face immediately broke with tears.

"Glenn, am I in a nursing home?"

"Honey, you are in a rehabilitation center. They are going to try to help you get better here."

"This looks like a nursing home. Are you sure?"

I was beginning to feel like a liar. "Sweetie, the sign out front says, *Anglican River Health and Rehabilitation.* They have a whole department on the end of the building that is dedicated to physical therapy. Let's give it a chance."

"Glenn, am I in a prison?"

"No! You are not in a prison. You can leave here anytime you want."

"Okay. We'll try it," she conceded for the time being.

The first day of any new place was one of transition and becoming acquainted with the surroundings. Part of Karen's new surroundings was her roommate, a lady in her seventies whose name was Luella. Luella would become a dear soul to Karen.

4

A Wilderness Experience

Karen had been in the hospital several times throughout her life. She was there several times for the birth of our children, a teenage car wreck and for other procedures. Hospitals have some familiarity to us. Nursing homes did not have familiarity to us. The nursing home would be one daily wilderness experience.

Nursing homes are not hospitals. You are likely thinking, "Of course they aren't. Everybody understands they are not hospitals." I understood a nursing home setting was not the very same as a hospital but when the residency purports the establishment has medical care, nurses and therapists then it has the image of offering medical care.

Experience is life's best educator. You can't learn how to drive a car until you sit behind a wheel. You can't learn to swim until you get into the water. You will never comprehend nursing homes until you spend six months in one. My comprehension of the Anglican River Nursing Home would be as a husband going to see my wife once and even twice daily. My comprehension of the facility would develop as I would see the care of the other residents, complaints of the nursing home aides, and how my wife was treated.

The person who developed the real comprehension of the nursing home life was Karen. While I tried to be there throughout the duration of the experience there was no way that I could even begin to understand the kind of nightmare she was awakening to and going to sleep at night facing.

Did the nursing staff, aides and administration unmercifully do evil things to her at all hours of the day? No. As I will write throughout this book some of the nurses were incredibly good to Karen. Some of the aides were good and wonderful. Some of the people who worked in other areas of the nursing home care team were excellent in their efforts. I believe one nurse saved Karen's life one night. She was fighting a horrible upper respiratory infection unable to cough up secretions from the infection for the entire night, and Dottie worked with Karen almost her entire shift keeping her from strangling to death on her own saliva and secretions from the infection. She was like a hero to us. But it almost killed Dottie. She was the only nurse on the entire wing of our nursing home. While she was giving Karen so much attention, all the other residents had to wait on their nighttime medications and other nursing care they received each night.

I could tell the next night that Dottie did not have the same level of energy for helping Karen. She was worn out from the sheer exhaustion of the demands of her job.

A part of the wilderness experience was learning that nursing homes are so very, very incredibly understaffed. One of the Anglican River aides confided in me, "I was the only aide for 66 patients one night." She went on to say, "A part of my job was to turn Karen over every two hours during my third shift. I never saw Karen on my shift. It was impossible to even make it to her room."

Karen does not have the ability to turn herself over. Her disease has progressed to the stage where it requires someone literally turning her over in bed. There were many, many nights when by the own testimony of this aide that Karen was never turned over. Can you imagine for even a moment what it must be like to be in bed for ten or twelve hours and not be able to be turned over?

Since Karen does not have any use of her arms or hands she couldn't use her call light to beckon a nurse. However, she had Luella. Luella was the sweet, incredible roommate who on so very many occasions would get out of her bed and walk to the door and look down the long hall to see if she could spot a nurse or nurse's aide to ask for help. While Karen could not turn her nurse's call light on, Luella could. But often it would stay on for the duration of the night without anyone coming to inquire about the nature of the need.

On many occasions Luella would literally walk down the hall holding onto the rail on the side of the wall balancing her self as she would go and summon someone to come and help Karen. Often it would be for more than just to turn Karen over. While Karen was at Anglican River during her last four months, she would run a 100 to 101 degree fever. Many of the nights would be unbearable, as she could not turn herself over, lying in a 101-degree fever, without anybody to even give her a cold washcloth for her fever or some Tylenol or Advil to subdue it.

Part of the wilderness experience was trying to understand this scenario of inattention. What was the big deal about turning my wife over in bed? These were persons whose job descriptions included turning the invalid patients over in bed.

The sheer neglect of Karen gave her a bed sore the size of an orange and almost three inches deep. A staph infection set in from most likely this bedsore that got into her blood stream and almost took her life. There is more to come about this later.

A part of this wilderness experience surely included the scenario of being the youngest person in the facility. We expect to admit loved ones in a nursing home when they are 77 not when they are 47. Thirty years is a lot of life and hopefully people will have the opportunity to enjoy each day to the fullest. Unfortunately we have no promises of longevity and especially healthy longevity.

While my wife has the ability to make friends like no one I've ever seen, having her daily environment of constant sick, aged, and some almost comatose people was difficult.

Once Karen was taken out of her wheelchair and put in bed there was nothing she could do except verbally communicate. Any one could come into her and Luella's room, go through their closets and dresser drawers and there was little they could do except ask them to leave and that wasn't always effective.

For several months Karen and Luella had a resident who lived down the hall from them who had Alzheimer's. She wondered the halls at all hours of the day and night. On many occasions Karen and Luella would awaken in the night and this lady would be in their room, standing over their beds, going through their closets and even worse trying to get in bed with them.

Imagine most every night you go to sleep you wonder, *What time will that person be in my room going through my closet stuff. What time will I be awakened by that person trying to climb into bed with me?* You wouldn't like it neither did Karen or Luella.

Luella would confide in me several times, "Glenn, I don't like that woman coming into our room. She scares me."

Imagine trying to sleep at night but only to be awakened by someone staring into your face. In Karen and Luella's case they were fortunate that the woman was believed to not be dangerous. However, I want to accentuate "believed." In the woman's state of mind she could have unintentionally harmed Karen. She could have tripped on an I V tube, fell on the bed and smothered her, got tangled in her catheter bag tube or jabbed her with something sharp.

Nursing homes for good reasons have doors without locks meaning any resident can leave his or her room, walk down the hall and come right into your room and try to do anything they can to you. In most cases any resident that would try to do something to you in a harmful way would be obviously out of his or her mind. This thought is not any more comforting than someone saying, "Timothy McVeigh was out of his mind when he bombed the Oklahoma Federal Building and killed all those people. It doesn't make us feel any better to say that the driver who hit our child was drunk. The child is dead still the same. It should not make us feel any better to say, *Oh, those people in the nursing home are just old and senile.* Some of those old senile people are dangerous.

A lady in a nursing home was murdered in our town. Another patient came into her room during the night and strangled her. The person that committed the murder was out of his mind. Does that make the family of the murdered loved one feel any better?

One of the wilderness findings of nursing home care is that often they have residents that they cannot handle and should not have as a resident.

Would you house your father, mother or spouse in a dangerous place? Would you place them in a place filled with strangers and some of them may have very violent tendencies? Your answer is likely a resounding, *No . . . never would I.* When you place someone you love in a nursing home, you are taking that risk. You do not know who lives across the hall. You are unsure as to what kind of person their roommate is until you get to know them. We were blessed in that Luella and her family were absolutely wonderful. But not everyone is as fortunate as we were from the roommate standpoint.

The loved one is placed in a home normally were everyone is a complete stranger and suffering from all kinds of illnesses that sometimes make them have some very weird behaviors. Your loved one ends up being on the brunt end of these behaviors.

Another part of the wilderness is that nursing homes have all kinds of people who work in them. Many of the assistants and aides don't even have high school educations. They are people in most cases working for minimum wage. They are people who have the choice of making minimum wage flipping hamburgers at McDonald's or changing and emptying bedpans at a nursing home.

Which job would you prefer . . . flipping hamburgers or putting bedpans under people's bottoms and emptying them all day? I am not berating either of the jobs. Both jobs render an incredible service to our society. The only point I am making is that the people who will care for your loved one are not highly educated skilled nurses. The nursing home will have a few nurses with their level of needed education to obtain their licenses but for the most part, the people who will feed, bathe, clothe and turn your loved one over are people who are trying to figure out how they can pass the GED high school diploma equivalency test.

If, we could go into the average nursing home and do a background check on some of these aides who care for our loved ones it would literally scare us to death as to the people who are taking care of mom or dad or our beloved husband or wife. This statement is in no way an indictment of every nursing home worker. I would venture to say that the majority of the employees are honest, capable, hard working people. Unfortunately it only takes a few incapable people on staff to give a nursing home a bad name. What if your mother or spouse is the one cared for by these incompetent people? It's one matter to hear of other people being cared for by incompetent people. It's another matter when it's your loved one being cared for by these people.

5

Sad, Lonely, Forgotten People

No one wants the description of his or her life to be the title of this chapter—sad, lonely and forgotten. Unfortunately much of the nursing home population spends their days in bed or in wheelchairs stationed in hallways or in front of televisions. While the nursing home, wherever it may be in America, may offer exercise classes, crafts, and opportunities to participate in organized activities, they meet the needs of only the functioning residents.

If the loved one has had a stroke, he cannot go down the hallway to do the exercise class nor can he join in the group sing-a-long in the dining hall. It's always possible that an aide may push your loved one down the hall to wherever the activity is occurring but who wants to sit and watch other people have fun if you can't in some semblance join in?

There is a population of people in American nursing homes that are very functional. They are able to walk to the dining hall for meals, do group exercise and walk out to the family car for a joy ride with their family. On a few, very few, occasions I have seen people in nursing homes that I thought had no business of being a resident. They seemed healthy enough to be living with family. The likely problem is that they had no family or no other place to go. The person may have had children but the children would not have mom or dad in their home to care for them.

There are always a multitude of reasons why people are in nursing homes. Sometimes life is such that a son or daughter does not have the physical or financial ability to have mom or dad to live with them for their remaining five or ten years. People have jobs that do not lend themselves to keeping a parent or other loved one in their home. Career or employed people are away from the house eight or ten hours at a time. When they come home they have nothing left physically or emotionally to give to the frail parent.

It is out of these and many other scenarios that parents may end up in nursing homes. Hopefully, it is a place where the parent will have a safe place to sleep, food to eat and medical care if it is necessary. Loved ones who are placed in nursing homes and are unable to walk out the door to a car and go somewhere are stranded.

Karen asked me on more than one occasion, "Am I in prison?" On the surface it almost sounds like a funny question. Consider the reality of this question. The nursing home resident does not have a car to jump into and escape the nursing home environment. Obviously in almost all the situations they are too sick, old or frail to be driving a car. They are dependent on a friend or family member to stop by and give them a ride somewhere—anywhere.

The nursing home resident may be able to step outside the home and walk around the grounds of the facility. But often, such facilities may have very limited grounds for such walks or be dangerously close to a highway.

People in nursing homes are put to bed at hours as early as seven in the evening and often allowed to sleep until ten in the morning. The rational of the aides is that if they are in bed then nothing care-wise has to be done for them.

When your life becomes a life being put to bed so early and staying in bed so late and then all you do during the day is eat three meals then what kind of life is that? The resident of the nursing home gains permission from the nursing staff as to when they may leave the facility. The resident is under strict watch as to what they eat, whom they see as a guest, when they leave the facility and what they can do in the facility.

Nursing homes work hard to make sure they interfere with the resident's life as much as possible. This is one area where nursing homes are very competent. They employ social workers and head of nursing directors and administrators. These people are very diligent in becoming involved in the personal lives of their residents and their families.

While the administrator, the head of nursing or social worker was never in Karen's room more than two or three times during her entire six month tenure at Anglican River, they certainly kept an eye out for how many times I took her out for lunch, a drive in the car or helped her change clothes in her room. While they were busy keeping watch over every personal activity of our family, they let Karen almost die from fever and staph infection.

Nursing homes are not prisons. But they surely must have this feel to a resident who is incapacitated in such a place twenty-four hours a day and seven days a week.

These are the people who sit in the hallways placed there by the nursing home staff. In the morning they are gotten out of bed, dressed and placed in a wheelchair and sat in the hall. For six months I went to Anglican River almost every day. Every day I saw the same dozen or more people on Karen's wing sitting in the hallway. Their heads were slumped down; they looked depressed and so very lonely. I would always try to make eye contact and smile at them and say hello. At first glance they would appear to be unable to respond verbally. Surprisingly, some of these people were very conversational. Most of them were desperate for someone to say something to them. Day by day their custom was to be taken out of bed and placed in a chair and stuck in the hallway where they would sit the duration of the day.

Some of these people had the ability to push themselves a little bit in their wheelchairs. They could be seen trudging slowly down the hallway with their heads bowed and their expressions downcast.

One such resident told me he had not had a visitor in weeks. He had a child in another town two hours away but he seldom came and when he did it was only for a brief visit.

Nursing homes are often the land of forgotten people—warehoused away from active society until such time that they can be placed in a casket and permanently removed from bothering anybody. Sound cruel? True.

We hear all the time when someone dies . . . *It's such a relief.* Yes, when we see our mom or dad suffer relentlessly it tears our hearts out for them to go through such agonizing discomfort. However, it's hard on us. It tears our hearts out because they are going through so much discomfort and agony. When they die the relief is that they no longer have to go through the daily misery but it's a relief to us who have to see them in their condition knowing there is nothing we can do to help them.

The pain of loved ones begins long before their downward spiral to death. We can't deal with seeing them sick and so we say, *Death is a relief.* Sadly we can't deal with them being old, senile or immobile. We put them in a nursing home and sigh, *we now can go on with our lives.* The cold truth is that we don't want to be bothered with people. We didn't mind mom and dad being around when they could help us with our homework or cook a meal for us. We didn't mind them being around when they were able to maintain a roof over our heads. Mom and dad were useful when they were helping us through college, but now that they are no longer useful to us, we put them away in nursing homes. Why? Because they are in the way of what we feel is daily normalcy. Daily normalcy is doing our jobs and going about our routines without having to have the load of another person weighing us down.

Dressing somebody, pushing somebody around in a wheelchair and having to care for them is beyond our daily frame of reference. We don't want to be bothered with them.

A friend of mine was telling me about caring for her sick husband for four weeks before he died. She even one day emptied his catheter she said with self-admiration. I said, "Wow, you are such a hero. I've emptied my wife's catheter for five years and pulled bowel movements out of her colon almost daily." The fact that she helped her husband a few weeks is admirable. But unfortunately we've reached such a state of mind in our country that if we give our mother or father an aspirin or get up with them a few times to take them to the bathroom then we feel we are such heroes.

A friend of mine that was a great peer while growing up took care of his sick wife for over 25 years. When you have cared for a loved one, day after day after day, then you have earned the right to talk about what you've done for your parent or spouse.

I'm not saying that everybody can keep their parent or loved one at home. Most people can't. We are so busy with jobs, careers, hobbies and our children who truly need us that we don't have anything left for a sick person. And, someday our spouse or children will likely not have time for us either.

Do you want to go to the nursing home when you are sick or old? I can hear you saying, *Glenn, I can't wait to get into a nursing home somewhere. That will be such a grand life for me.* Of course you are not saying that because that is not where you want to spend the last few years or months of your life. What makes you think that's where your spouse or parent wants to spend their last few months? In so many cases we have no other choice, but let's be realistic. Your loved one does not want to go there; and it's a lousy place to spend one's last days.

Karen has said on several occasions, "Glenn please let me die at home. It's better for anybody to die at home or even in the hospital but not in a nursing home. It would be better for these people to die in their homes and at least be happy than to live their remaining days at Anglican River unattended and uncared for. It would be better for them to fall in the floor and be found dead; at least then they would have died happy."

My wife's response is probably similar to others. I can't speak for every nursing home resident in America. Surely there are some who if they had the opportunity would take the podiums, lecture circuits and all media outlets and proclaim how wonderful it is to live in a nursing home. They would surely speak about all their freedom, good sleeping quarters, good food and the great environment they live in. I don't believe that for one minute. I believe there are many who are in nursing homes who are so sick and so mentally incapable that they are not able to imagine being back in normal, daily society. I do know there are scores of people in nursing homes who are very mentally coherent and physically competent to feed, clothe and bathe themselves. They hate their environment. They detest having to daily listen to the cries of other people who live down the hall from them. They are sick of seeing the same food week after week and in some places almost day after day. They are sick and tired of being in daily situations where they have to be fearful of other patients coming into their rooms and either robbing or assaulting them.

In so many cases the nursing home resident is put there because the family felt they had no choice. In other cases they are often put there against their will.

Anglican River had a resident who lived down the hall from Karen who talked a lot about how her son had just dumped her into the nursing home. He had power of attorney and moved her out of her house, placed her in the nursing home and sold the family house. He took her life's savings and moved to another state. She often lamented, "I can't believe my son did this to me. He has only come back a couple of times to see me."

Another lady at Anglican River constantly walked the halls. "I hate this place," she sighed to me one day as I walked in the direction of Karen's room. "I don't want to be here but my children got control of my life and put me in here. I'm stuck. I'm helpless. I can't see anyway out of here."

On one such Friday night she was dressed and sitting in the foyer. A lady friend of hers was supposed to come and take her out for dinner. She was excited to be getting a break from the nursing home. "I can't wait to get out of here for couple of hours."

I could only wonder about what would become of her. If she were healthy and mentally alert, she wouldn't stay that way very long. The toll of being around so many depressed, lonely and very sick people would eventually catch up with her.

The hallways of America's nursing homes tell a sad story. The story is of isolation, depression and discouragement almost unto death. The nursing home in America is commonly thought of as the *last stop of life before death.* If you go to the hospital, you have hopes of being helped back to health. When you go to the nursing home in our country, it is with the knowledge that this is where you will live until you die. The resident is placed in a room with a small half bed and a bulletin board to post a few favorite pictures. This little relegated corner becomes one's last physical earthly move and it is here where life in this world will cease.

Ministers, funeral home directors, medical people and folks from all walks of life often speak about the nursing home as people's final stop in this life. Therefore, our country has allowed the nursing home industry to warehouse people, while drawing billions of our tax dollars to give them beds and some semblance of care until such time that they can die. People in nursing homes line the hallways, sit in corners of their rooms, hang their heads in dining halls, and wail helplessly for attention . . . knowing their time is running out and in many cases no one cares or is doing anything about helping them. They are afraid, lonely and forgotten. The nursing home administration and staff likes it this way.

Nursing homes are so understaffed and the staff in most cases is so underpaid that they don't have much time to give a lot of individual attention to the residents. If the resident has family in every day then they are pressured into taking care of the resident.

Many nursing home residents go days without baths. They go days without having their teeth brushed or hair combed. They may sit or lay in a bowel movement all day. If a family member is coming, often the nursing home staff feels more pressure to make an effort to at least bathe and care for the resident. Residents who do not have family members dropping by and asking questions and showing strong interests in what is going on will be neglected unmercifully.

Unfortunately, even with me going daily to visit with Karen, the staff at Anglican River would let her go for entire weekends without a bath. Often I would clean up a bowel movement that Karen had laid in for the day. Many mornings when I would go in to see her I would discover she had been put to bed without having her teeth brushed.

Remember, Karen was totally at the mercy of Anglican River for being fed, having her teeth brushed, and being bathed. She has no use of her hands, arms or legs. If she got fed, the staff fed her. If she was bathed, the nursing home staff bathed her. She truly requires an immense amount of care and attention. Yet, the nursing home was phenomenally compensated for her expected care, which was depressingly lacking.

The sad reality is that most of the nursing home residents in America are stuck in dead end nursing homes, sad, alone and forgotten.

Sometimes I hear a family member talk about his mother or spouse being in a nursing home and they will say something like, *they are taking such good care of her.* And then I will find out it's been six weeks since the family member has checked on his loved one. During this time, that loved one may have been lucky to have one or two baths a week and may have developed a bedsore the size of a softball due to the sheer neglect of the home. The loved one may have been physically abused by being verbally assaulted with remarks about them, *being a pain to take care of,* or *if you don't shut up, we are going to close the door and turn out the lights.*

Family members who do not check on their loved ones almost daily, have no real way of knowing exactly what kind of care they are receiving. But I don't blame a son or daughter for saying, *the nursing home is taking such good care of my mother or father.* If they are being cared for, then it is much easier to go on with life and think, *I don't have to do anything to help my mother or father or spouse. I can go on my merry way with life and not have to be burdened with concern.* This type of thinking is normally a false sense of mental comfort. It is delusional on the part of any family member to think they can walk away from a loved one in a nursing home and that the loved one will receive the utmost care and respect. The average American nursing home does not have the staff to give the utmost attention and care. They are filled with stressed out nurses who are tirelessly overworked by the administration. The administration works to please the owner of the nursing home. The owner of the nursing home wants a good profit. A good profit enables the nursing home owner or owners to have their yearly multiple six-figure incomes while the nursing home they own becomes a residence to a group of lonely and uncared for people.

6

Holidays
In The Nursing Home

Karen was checked into the Anglican River Nursing Home the first part of November. We knew Thanksgiving was coming along with Christmas. As a family we had no idea of how long Karen would be there. We did know that Thanksgiving was coming and every assurance was made that we would have Karen home for Thanksgiving. It would be our two children, Karen and I but at least the celebration would be in our home and out of the confines of the nursing home. The nursing home would have a turkey dinner in the main dining hall but we felt like holidays were meant for home.

Trying to cook a dinner for the holiday was out of the question. Fortunately for us, a local Cracker Barrel Restaurant would be open and carry out was available.

As I took Karen out of the home, I passed by the majority of the residents who had no one around to visit or take them out for the Thanksgiving occasion.

Bringing Karen home, the boys, she, and I would sit at our dining room table with what we had carried in. The carry in was great. Who wants to spend all day cooking? We ate our food and didn't have to worry about staring at leftovers.

Sitting at our dining room table, I fed Karen small pieces of turkey, dressing, sweet potatoes, and other holiday fare such as pumpkin pie. Pumpkin pie is one of Karen's favorites.

The hard part of Thanksgiving was the day ending and having to take Karen back to the nursing home. This was almost a form of hell in itself. Here our family celebrated a wonderful Thanksgiving Day and then at the end of day I have to load my wife back into our car and take her back to the nursing home. I know how I personally felt as I pushed her into the entrance of the facility, down the hallway and back into her room.

As I pushed her down the hall Karen had tears running down her face. Who wouldn't? Who would not be crying? Here is a beautiful 47-year-old woman with two teenage children and a husband at home. She leaves her comfortable home after a pleasant Thanksgiving experience to return back to hell. Who wouldn't have a few tears streaming down their face?

A nurse standing out in the hall had her medication cart that carried all the patient's medications. She saw Karen all teary eyed and became all interested, "Oh Karen what is going on with you? What is wrong?" She would follow us down to Karen's room where she again asked what was going on.

Try to get this scenario. My wife and I have just finished a pleasant day. It's agonizing for Karen to have to go back to this place of depression and nightmares and then we are followed to her room with this nurse asking, "What's wrong? What's wrong?"

I looked at the nurse and said, "We've had a fun day. She just is depressed."

"Well why is she depressed?" She asked.

"She would like to have stayed at her house."

"Karen, . . . are you okay?" the nurse pressed.

Crying by this time, Karen sobbed she was just fine.

The nurse walked out of the room and said she would be back.

Karen was teary eyed because the last place she wanted to spend Thanksgiving night was in the nursing home.

Later in a meeting with the nursing home administration workers, which consisted of the administrator, head of nursing and social worker, it would be called to my attention that Karen came back to the nursing home crying after one of our outings. The implication made by the administration was that I had done something out of line to make my wife cry. The implication was that I had in someway hurt her.

Karen and I were both disgusted by the implication. I simply said to these poor nursing home administrators, "She was depressed about coming back in here. Wouldn't you be depressed and teary eyed too?" They sat stone-faced looking at me like they couldn't understand what I was saying. I don't think they wanted to understand what I was saying.

Nursing home administrators never take the side of the family or for that matter the nursing home resident. The administration, social worker and head of nursing begin to formulate an offensive collection of any kind of data they can accumulate the day a resident checks into the facility. This collected material is what they use to protect themselves in any way they possibly can from lawsuits. Often it is material they use to launch attacks against the resident's family members and the resident. Or, it is material used to serve as their defense should a lawsuit be filed against them. The implication from the nursing home was that I had personally upset Karen.

Nursing home staff will never admit they are the ones who upset a loved one or do anything detrimental to them physically or emotionally. They want to say their nursing home is a great place to live. They will talk about how wonderful everything at the nursing home is and they do not want a crying woman pushed down the hallway past other guests to in any way detract from their superficial promotion of their home being a great facility.

Anglican River like most other nursing homes is only great when the tour of the facility is given and when the papers are signed committing a resident to the facility so that they can bill Medicare or Medicaid for the multi thousands of dollars each month that they receive for each resident. Once a patient is moved into the home and the paper work is completed, then the nursing home quits selling itself. They know they don't need to because the resident will likely die there. The family checks in the resident, goes their own merry way and the loved one is left at their mercy . . . and there is no mercy. They know that most of the time the family does not take the resident out of the nursing home because the loved one is there because they do not feel they can care for them. It was work finding and selecting a home. It is more work to find another home and relocate the loved one. It is true this goes on but not as much as you might think. Other nursing homes are reluctant to take other residents from other nursing homes. They ask, "Why is your wife or father unhappy at her/his current facility?" They are afraid of dealing with problems and if you are an unhappy family member then they know they will have to deal with you—and they don't want to deal with unhappy family members.

Thanksgiving would be over and then would come Christmas. Karen loves Christmas. No person I have ever known worked any harder than did Karen on making Christmas special. Our house from room to room was decorated for Christmas. I'm not saying it was wall-to-wall decorations but she would make sure each room had something special to remind each of us of the Christmas season.

We had a pencil tree that Karen had purchased. Karen loved this little tree that only held a few lights. Each year she would cover it with Angels. I took this tree into Anglican River the first part of December covered with lights. I knew that being in the nursing home during

December would be emotionally painful. She loved shopping and baking and celebrating Christmas.

"Glenn will I be able to come home for Christmas?"

"Karen, we will see to it that you are home for Christmas."

"But, what about Christmas Eve. They won't let me spend the night at home."

"We will bring you home Christmas Eve in the early afternoon, and then bring you back here late."

Anglican River would not let our family ever keep Karen at home overnight. If she were not back in the facility by midnight they would not receive their money from Medicare. Please keep in mind: nursing homes are about money. There are a few church related nursing homes that work very hard at providing a ministry through their facility, but these places are few and are not necessarily able to provide any better care. Usually they are strapped by the same Medicare/Medicaid regulations as any other corporate nursing home and so life is not much different.

The difference may be in the overall attitude of the administration in trying to be more compassionate toward the family. This is not a fast rule and every nursing home facility is somewhat different in administrative leadership or corporate demands . . . but not much different.

As we approached the Christmas holiday Karen wanted to go Christmas shopping. She had one thing on her mind and that was buying me something for Christmas. I am deplorable when it comes to caring for watches and so Karen wanted me to have a new watch for Christmas.

"Glenn, I want you to pick out a new watch. I don't care how much it costs. I want you to have it for Christmas."

The last thing I wanted Karen to do was to spend a lot of money on a watch. We had a store in Evansvelle named Elder Beerman's that was having a going out of business sale. We decided to check it out hearing they had a nice sale on all of their merchandise. I found a Guess watch that was fifty percent off the marked price. The purchase was made.

It broke my heart that Karen had one thing on her mind and that was making sure I had something from her under our Christmas tree. While a Christmas gift was the last thing on my mind it was on the forefront of Karen's mind.

Karen had in mind a large tote bag. Several months prior when she had been to Elder Beermans with some friends she had spied a nice bag that she felt would be good for transporting clothes back and forth to the nursing home or hospital since she had been in and out so much. Plus, it would be attractive for overnight trips should those ever become an option again for her. We found the bag and took it and the watch to the customer service section of the store to have it gift wrapped for Christmas.

When Christmas Eve finally came, Karen's parents and sister came down from Dayton, Ohio. I brought Karen home where she spent the afternoon and wanted to relax in one of our recliners while several of us went to the Christmas Eve Service at church, which was held at 9 p.m.

I encouraged Karen to go, but the difficulty of talking to so many people and greeting so many folks in her condition was more than she could handle. Her mother stayed with her during the hour we were at church.

When we got back home it was after 10:00 and I knew by the time I got her back to the nursing home it would be eleven. It was difficult loading her into our van and taking her away from our home on Christmas Eve . . . back to a nursing home.

As I dropped her off, her roommate, Luella was delighted to see her. It had been a lonely night for Luella. Karen was company to her and she was so sweet to Karen that it eased the pain a little to have such a kind and coherent roommate.

The next day I was back at the nursing home by 10:00 in the morning to bring Karen home for Christmas Day. A Sunday school class at our church had performed a tremendous act of kindness in providing our Christmas dinner for us. They made everything for us. Our entire family was overwhelmed by not only all the food, but also how delicious it was.

We celebrated the day by opening gifts and sharing the scrumptious meal. Karen relaxed and napped in the afternoon. "Glenn, you just don't realize how great it is to sit here and sleep in my own home. I feel so safe to be in my own home. I feel like I can rest and not worry about anything happening to me."

That night about 8:00 Karen and I took the despondent ride back to Anglican River. The Christmas tree in the foyer of the nursing home was a reminder of the day we had just celebrated. Soon I would have Karen back into her room, undressed and ready for bed.

Karen always wanted me to change her clothes and put her in bed. "Glenn, the nurses aides on this shift are so rough when they change my clothes and lift me in bed. I feel like every time they do it they are tearing my arms off."

While Karen was at Anglican River her arms began to deteriorate to where she could no longer lift them. Plus it was excruciating for Karen for anybody to lift on her arms. Some of the aides seemed to purposely lift her by her arms when they put her to bed at night.

Time and again we asked about a mechanical lift that we even have in our home but the nursing home staff said they did not have one. Imagine a nursing home not having any mechanical devices for lifting people. I think the aides were just in a hurry to get it over with, put Karen to bed and get out of the room.

"Glenn thank you for putting me to bed. At least I'll be able to sleep a little better not having to hurt for hours from my arms being tugged and pulled on."

I kissed Karen goodnight. "Honey, I would give anything if I were not leaving you here."

"I would give anything if you were not leaving me here, too."

Assuring her I would see her the next day I hugged and kissed her again and went out of Anglican River to go back home where Karen's parents and my children would be watching Christmas movies.

There have been many firsts for Karen and I; but spending Christmas night with her in a nursing home was one of those "firsts" most middle age couples do not want to even think about let alone experience.

7

Dating Karen

One of my chief concerns in having Karen at Anglican River was her surviving daily depression from her surroundings. She was in a nursing home. She was the youngest person in the facility. She had two teenage kids at home that she missed terribly.

I could not dump her into the facility to walk away and never return. Some families and spouses do. Some spouses have checked their sick spouse into the facility, divorced them and never returned. The person stuck in the nursing home has no one to advocate or defend them and so they end up in a helpless situation of being relegated to a room where they have to wait upon the good graces of whomever might stop by or offer any kind of help to them.

I was committed to taking Karen out of the nursing home facility as often as was possible with her health and my schedule. There was never a week her first five months that I did not take her out of the facility at least twice a week. There were some weeks where I took her as many as three times.

Sometimes these outings would only be for a couple of hours. Karen liked to go out and eat fried cheese sticks from a local Sonic

Drive-In Restaurant. We could pull right up to the ordering station and sit for an hour or two and just talk.

Having a conversation at Anglican River was impossible. Luella was so great. There were times when she would literally take her chair and go out into the hall so that Karen and I could visit. We never asked her to and told her whenever she did that she didn't have to leave the room. "Oh you kids need your privacy," she would say.

Most of the time when I was at Anglican River an aide or sometimes more than one would be in and out of our room. A couple of aides would almost hang out in Karen's room while I was there making small talk. Sometimes they would talk about dreading to go down the hall and do something for someone that was difficult to care for. I got the impression that they were camping out in Karen's room except for when she really needed them to do something.

The fact that aides were always around made it impossible for Karen and I to talk about anything. We couldn't talk that much about the kids, church or anything personal. Taking Karen out of the facility was the only way we could have a conversation.

While Karen was at Anglican River we would celebrate our 25th wedding anniversary. We talked about going out to eat but Karen didn't feel like making the restaurant scene. She was unable to feed herself. She had developed severe tremors in her hands, arms and even her head was shaking. Eating food with somebody feeding it to her was a chore within itself.

We celebrated the day quietly by me bringing her to our home. I had flowers for her and a new watch that she would wear for a couple of months until she began to fear one of the aides at the nursing home was going to steal it. Karen slept so soundly at night because of the tremendous amount of medication the nursing home was giving her; that she knew anyone could easily slip the watch over her arm and she would never know who took it.

The first date Karen and I had was with Jim and Anne Falkenberg of Ohio. Jim and Anne set it up for me to meet them and Karen at a pizza place in Dayton. When the pizza was done they said they had to leave and said they were going to just let me take Karen home without even asking Karen if she wanted to ride back with me. She was stuck. I looked at her and kind of uncomfortably said, "I'll have you home in ten minutes." From the outset Karen was not very excited about me taking her home. But we sat in her driveway of her home and talked that night for two hours and were married six months later.

There is something about getting away from all distractions to have an intimate conversation. Two people can talk anywhere and it would be sad if you had to leave the house every time you needed a conversation but occasionally you need to just get away to talk.

Karen and I were together three and four times a week leading up to our wedding. Our courtship was short and two people cannot get to know each other in six months. Karen and I continued to learn about each other the first 25 years of our marriage. Most people will continue to learn about their spouse their whole lives. There is no such thing as being with somebody a year and being able to say, *I know all there is to know about my husband or wife.*

One reason we are always learning about our spouse is because our spouse is always changing. People change. The person you knew once upon a time in high school is no longer the exact same person. Some of the characteristics and personality traits will remain the same but people go through experiences in life that mature them, break them and remold them. People go through divorces, raise kids, and have educational experiences that affect their outlook on life and how they deal with life. A couple that quits trying to know their spouse will soon not know them.

As a minister I have talked to hundreds of couples. One of the chief concerns that always comes out of the sessions will be this statement: *I don't know this man anymore.* I hear husbands say the same about their wives. *She has changed so much. I don't even know her anymore.*

People change. God does not change, but people do. Time and experiences and good times and bad times and events all have a way of shaping and making us different than we were twenty or maybe even ten years ago. Therefore, it is vital that we continue to work on knowing each other. When we cease to know each other then we don't know how to love each other and when we can't love each other the relationship is history in the sense of it being a real and meaningful relationship.

This is why we have so many people living together today unhappily married. They are living with someone they don't know. This comes about because two people became so busy and so preoccupied with life that they quit dating. When people are dating, what is happening? They are talking.

Go into any restaurant and look around. How do you know which people are married and which people are out on a date? The people talking to each other are the ones who aren't married. I've seen this too many times because by habit I look for it. This is not a hard fast rule because there are many good marriages where people constantly continue to work on the marriage relationship. The big factor in the marriage staying together and getting better is a continued effort by the couple to continue talking and dating.

Muscles that are not worked go away. An athlete may get into incredible shape but he stays in shape by maintaining a weekly regiment of the right exercise and eating habits.

Couples start out dating. They start out meeting for a drink, a lunch and during those meetings there is conversation and normally if there is interest, the people are intently listening to each other and sharing of themselves.

Twenty-five years later a lot of marriages have quit talking and intently listening to the other marriage partner. Therefore the marriage gets into trouble and so often others are found to talk to and the marriage dissolves.

Why is it so important for the communication of the marriage partners to be a priority? Because I say it again, people change. You are changing. And while we see changes in people these changes need to be talked about with the spouse. This doesn't mean that we sit down and say, *let me tell you how I have changed this week.* As you talk about your life and what is going on in your life and how you feel about certain things then your spouse knows what is going on with you. You then are able to hear his/her responses about life and therefore there is mutual sharing. This mutual sharing is enabling you to know the heart of your spouse and respond accordingly in your marriage efforts.

All marriages are work. Some marriages may be less work or more work than others but regardless there is work involved or the marriage becomes empty and dead.

While Karen and I went through difficult valleys as she progressed in her disease, one of the saving factors was our three and four outings a week. Even the weekend before Karen would end up back in the hospital and then in the nursing home we were at Garfield's Restaurant in Evansvelle eating lunch celebrating Zachary's fifteenth birthday. She wasn't able to feed herself very well and so it was difficult for her to be in public but we managed to have a conversation with all four of us in a noisy restaurant.

With a long pattern of going out I couldn't bear to not have those moments with Karen even though she was now living in a nursing home.

The first time I picked Karen up at the nursing home I asked the nurse at Karen's station if it would be a problem to take her out. "Of course not, just have her back by 12:00 midnight or Medicare won't pay us." I agreed and about an hour later took her out.

We rode around in our van for an hour or so, got something to drink, talked in the car and then headed home where I let Karen sit in one of our recliners for a couple of hours and watch television. She hadn't been home since spending two weeks in the hospital and a week in the nursing home and it felt great for her to be home.

When we got back to the nursing home I was resoundingly scolded by one of the nurses, "You didn't tell us you were taking Karen out."

"Yes I did. I told Sammie we were going."

"Mr. Mollette, whenever you take her out, you be sure you stop at this desk and tell us."

Again I repeated myself, "Sammie knew we were going."

"Yes she did," she finally acknowledged, "But you have to take her medication with you when you go."

"Oh I didn't know that, " I acknowledged. "Next time I'll be sure to pick it up."

It had never been communicated to me the protocol of leaving the nursing home with Karen. No one from the administration or nursing or social worker staff ever communicated to me the procedure for signing Karen out or picking up her medication for the several hours that we would be out of the facility.

This would be how everything would be learned or communicated from the staff at Anglican River Nursing Home. All communication would be after the fact.

An ounce of prevention is worth a pound of cure. A little information and orientation is a wonderful preclude to circumventing unnecessary misunderstanding and friction.

There was never a time that I was asked to sign Karen out of Anglican River until the last month of our stay in the facility. This is something that any real nursing home would require of anybody. For example almost any respectable looking person could enter Anglican River and push a resident right out the door and no one in the facility would know what had happened to the resident. The signing out procedure is something any facility should require of any one taking a resident out of the nursing home.

I can't imagine how Anglican River was able to operate their first two years without having this policy intact. And if they had this policy of signing someone out of the facility they never asked me to sign Karen out until her last month of residency.

One of the problems of taking Karen out for joy rides, lunch or any outing was that it required the nursing home staff to bathe and dress Karen. Often I wanted to pick her up at 11 a.m., which meant they would have to begin by 9:00 a.m. the process of putting her together. This meant it required the energy and efforts of two staff members. The nursing home staff was spread so thin that concentrating this much on one patient was difficult. There were 139 other patients in the facility.

, Sadly, any and every patient in a nursing home deserves a bath and attention in getting properly dressed for the day. It is further sad that the average nursing home does not employ enough nursing aides to adequately do the job without everybody in the facility being constantly stressed out from the workload demand.

For over six months seeing my wife in a nursing home was like dating her but in a very eerie, scary way. Like any good date she was always glad to see me and sad sometimes to tears when I walked out the door waving goodbye to her. Calling ahead and letting the staff know I was coming to pick her up was like making all the arrangements to see my girl—kind of like when we first dated. When we first started out it was a simple phone call and an agreed upon time for me to pick her up. We didn't really care what the agenda was for the date we just wanted to be together.

The nursing home scenario of seeing each other had a couple of similarities in that I had to call ahead when I picked her up. Karen didn't much care what we would be doing nor did I, we were together and that was all that mattered.

But our new dating lifestyle was difficult as we now had nurses, aides and nursing home administration that observed our coming and going. Our dates were better documented in the nursing home records than the number of times that Karen was turned over in bed to keep her from getting a huge bedsore. The nursing home aides were more interested in our personal lives than in making sure Karen didn't sit in her wheelchair for five hours in a row with her head dangling backwards off the headrest because the headrest had become twisted. I was amazed at how quickly an aide could find herself to Karen's room if I walked in and sat down to talk to my wife. But I was further amazed that they couldn't seem to find the time to clean up a bowel movement my wife had laid in for hours or change a catheter bag.

It was this kind of stress that added a new dimension to our new cycle of dating each other. The lifestyle of nursing home care and treatment was the obvious main topic of our conversations as we visited with each other in our home, sat at Sonic Drive-In, or drove around the community.

Many dating couples talk about life in general. They talk about their work or school, family or career aspirations. Karen and I talked a lot about life in the nursing home. We wish the conversations could have been about how great life was in the nursing home. But life is not great in nursing homes. The food is bad and the places are too understaffed to do the work adequately. The needs of the average nursing home residents are far above and beyond what the home is able to adequately offer.

Administrators and corporations who own them can lie about this and argue that I am off base—but I'm not.

Patients are told to "Wait awhile. We will take care of you later." Three hours later an aide may show back up if they remember that you needed something. Patients are told to shut up. Patients often have their doors shut so that the aides in the facility will not have to hear what they are being asked to do.

One area daughter tells of placing a tape recorder in her dad's room in another nursing home. She picked up a recording of the nurses slapping her dad and talking very ugly to him. The state health department where she turned the tape in did nothing but issue a two-day citation to the nursing home facility. It meant nothing more than a slap on the wrist.

All relationships can continue to grow in different ways. Our marriage was growing through this developing nursing home nightmare. Our dates were brief sessions of relief for Karen as I'm sure any brief departure from a nursing home would be for anyone.

What I was hearing from Karen about her daily care was very much concerning me. How could a place so new and nice with supposedly a good reputation be doing all the things that Karen said they were doing or not doing?

Later I would do some research on the Internet and discover that Anglican River had one of the poorest ratings of care of any nursing home facility in our area. In almost every category of care they rated poorly in comparison to most of the other nursing homes in our region. What looks good on the outside may not be good on in the inside.

During our tenure at Anglican River they would have their license pulled for a couple of days by the health department. The reason was for the way they were treating an elderly man who was considered violent and dangerous to the other nursing home patients. The state department notified Anglican River that this man was never to be left in the room without an aide present. This kind of care was never given to the man because Anglican River was so understaffed. A local television station, WKAB picked up the information and made it a lead in story that Anglican River had their license suspended. The next day a reporter was out in the parking lot with his camera interviewing family members. Fortunately for Anglican River not one family member said anything negative about the nursing care facility. Fortunately for Anglican River the reporter asked the wrong people and didn't hang around long enough to talk to the right people. People who drop their loved ones off at facilities and only see them once a week are going to say, "Yes . . . this place is taking great care of my mom or dad." If they admitted to the truth that mom or dad is not being treated so good then that would require them to think about why they are letting them stay in a place that does not take good care of their loved one. And if they started answering tough questions like that then they would have to ask another tough question, "What am I going to do about my mom's or dad's care?"

This means they would have to think about either relocating mom or dad to another facility or bringing mom or dad to their house to live. Either of the decisions requires a lot of work and complicated transition. Therefore, it's easier on the family to just say to all those who ask: *sure, mom or dad or my spouse is receiving great care at the nursing home.* If great care means they keep the room warm or cool and dinner trays are delivered to the bedside three times a day then the resident may be receiving great care. But I think most families, when first thinking about placing a loved one in the nursing home, are looking for more than three meals a day and a warm room in the winter.

Unfortunately many families are ground down by the sheer toil of caring for a loved one and they hopelessly resign themselves to having to live with the guilt of placing them in a nursing care facility.

As I would drop Karen off from our outings I would often look at her window from the parking lot. I would see the window to the room to my young 47 year-old wife. I would go home to our two teenagers knowing that Anglican River was the last place in the world that Karen wanted to be or I wanted her to be.

On a few occasions the blinds to Karen's room were open enough to where I could see her sitting in her wheelchair. It was painful to see my wife of over twenty-five years relegated to being positioned in an electric chair, watching television, dependent on the nursing home staff to do something for her whenever they could get around to it. Driving out of the parking lot with that being the last image I would see was horrifying.

Twenty-five years prior Karen would stand in her door and wave to me when I dropped her off at her home after one of our dinner or movie dates. I would go back home with feelings of love and anticipation that boyfriends have after they've been with the love of their lives.

The nursing home did not change those feelings of love and anticipation. My love for Karen only grew while she was a resident and my anticipation became a daily hope that somehow life could be made better and easier for her.

8

Third Shift Horror

There were very few nights that I did not leave my wife with her condition being sheer dread. Her countenance and tone in her voice only underscored her sincerity when she told me how awful the nights at Anglican River were.

I asked her, "Karen, is there any one that is hurting you?"

"No one is beating me. It's not like that. But there is no help available. If it weren't for Luella I don't know what I would do."

Luella was very functional both mentally and physically. Her balance was not good and she had fallen and broke her arm. In time her arm slowly began to heal and function normally.

"Glenn, it's the male nurse. He will do nothing to help me. He comes into this room, flips on the lights, almost throws my medicine down my throat; and then turns them out and almost runs out the door. He will not take one second to listen to me. He will not do one thing to help me."

Karen would ask Max to turn her over in bed. She was not able to move, shift and especially turn herself in bed. The dayshift nurse had said they were supposed to turn her over every two hours to prevent bedsores. The nurse told me this, but the follow through of turning

Karen over every two hours was not happening during the day nor was it especially happening during the night.

The dayshift nurses and second shift nurses were definitely more on top of their nursing skills than what the third shift was. However, there were nurses and aides that worked all shifts who were just going through the motions of being on their jobs. Any human being can just show up at work and produce very little. Maybe the employee is having a bad time at home. Maybe they have sick kids or a bad marriage and they bring all these problems with them to work and they have all this on their minds while they are trying to perform their tasks. I would give any nursing home employee the benefit of the doubt that they are humanly prone to have bad days just like any other person.

The fact that nursing home employees are not abundantly paid does not help. Nurses make okay wages. But nursing homes in comparison to most hospitals and upper care level medical facilities do not pay as well. The aides work for almost as little as minimum wage in many nursing home facilities. These are the people who do most of the dirty work such as turning patients, bathing them, dressing them, cleaning them up after a bowel movement, feeding them and anything that has any semblance of toil or hard work. It has to be very frustrating to an aide to work her self to exhaustion knowing that her paycheck won't be enough for her to feed her own kids.

"Glenn, when Max comes in here and I ask him to turn me over he simply ignores me and walks right back out the door."

"Glenn, she's telling you the truth," chimed in Luella. He just walks out the door."

I would later find out from an aide that Max did this all the time not only to Karen but also to other patients who needed him. He was the only nurse working third shift and he was all that the patients on Karen's wing had. An aide who quit Anglican River after they had made her take care of 66 patients by herself on third shift told me, "Glenn, I caught Max several times turning on Karen's call light and walking out of the room. Instead of him staying in the room and doing whatever she was asking him to do, he would turn on the call light and leave it for an aide to do. But Glenn, sometimes it might be an hour or more before we would even see the call light. If I was at the facility and down at the other end of the hall I could go for a couple of hours before seeing a call light over Karen's door. Even then it didn't mean that I would be able to go directly and help her."

Max had a very casual "sit on your butt," attitude about nursing. There were a few times that I got up and went to the nursing home in the middle of the night to just turn Karen over in bed or see if she needed anything. I never went that I didn't see Max sitting at the nurse's station desk and usually reading a newspaper. The hallways were quiet and any would be spectator would surmise that everything was in order. It would depend on your definition of order. The order was basically that all the residents had been knocked out for the night with sleeping pills so they would sleep eight or more hours without bothering anybody.

Karen was being knocked out as well. The sleeping medicine that she was being given at nine or ten o'clock at night would often sedate her to where nothing could wake her. Except, when she would lie in one motionless position for five hours or more she would awaken feeling like her neck or back was breaking.

Imagine how many times you roll over in bed every night. It's hard for us to do because we've likely never had any one count for us how many times we roll over. But not only do we roll over, but also we change positions throughout the night. Karen's disease had progressed to where she couldn't even move or restation her arms. It's a horrendous situation for anyone in life to be in. We so take for granted our smallest physical motor abilities.

The nurse's aide also confessed to me, "Glenn, I know there were nights that Karen was never turned. I personally could not get to her. I had so many patients that some nights I could never see Karen.

The hardest part of the nights for Karen became her sheer neglect. Luella was often trudging down the hallway trying to find an aide that would come and turn Karen over, give her some medicine or help her in some other way. But there were many times Luella would go to the doorway, look down the hall and see not one single nurse or aide in sight.

The third shift would start as early as 11:00. They only had to be in the facility eight hours. After eight hours they would leave to go on about life. The nursing home resident is stuck in the facility in most cases twenty-four hours a day.

There were times when the heat in the room would become unbearable. Each room had its own separate furnace/air conditioner. During the winter one aide would adjust the heat in the evening but by two in the morning it might become eighty degrees in the room or hotter. Nursing homes have to keep their rooms warmer than average it seems because of the elderly who are more prone to being cold in normal temperatures than active people. But even the sick can get too hot.

Karen would often get stuck with having a couple of sheets over her and sleeping right beside the furnace putting out unstoppable heat. Excessive heat is very difficult on multiple sclerosis patients. Somehow beyond my understanding, the heat induces their bodies to tighten and makes them highly more anxious.

Karen had to go to a wheelchair in April 1995. At night I remember her becoming so hot that she would get into her wheelchair, go to the backdoor of our house, and sit with the door open trying to get some cool air. I thought it was crazy because there were times that it was the dead of winter and our furnace thermostat would never be set more than sixty-eight degrees at night. Yet Karen would be burning up. Sitting in the doorway with the door wide open and the snow flying outside seemed to ease whatever she was feeling.

It's impossible for any caregiver of a person with multiple sclerosis to understand what the person with the disease is feeling. I think now after many years I am better able to respond when Karen says she is experiencing something or feeling a certain way. Multiple sclerosis is a terrible disease for the person who has it and very difficult for the caregiver to know how to respond to. The medical world cannot even deal with multiple sclerosis so how can a caregiver understand how to grapple with the disease? The patient tries daily to understand the disease and how to battle all the physical complications it produces.

In the nursing home Karen couldn't get up and sit in a doorway in the dead of winter for relief of whatever she was feeling. She was trapped in a bed unable to move. She had to often face a furnace producing heat of over eighty degrees directly on her already overheated body. She was unable to turn her call light on for an aide or nurse to come and help her because she had gotten to the point where she could not lift her arm. She had developed tremors so bad that she did not have the steadiness to handle the call light or the button that even turned on her television. She was dependent on Luella, who at times was able to limp down the hallway holding onto the handrail in the hallway, to find her someone who might turn down the heat.

There were times even when Luella would go out and find an aide when no one would come in response to the call light. Normally the promise was made, "We will be there in a minute." But the minutes either became hours or until someone showed up on the first shift.

The absence of care on the third shift also meant that there would be many nights that Karen would lie in pain.

Karen's arms and hands would hurt her so badly that she would lay and cry. If a nurse or aide even looked like they might touch Karen's hands or arms it sent shock waves of pain throughout Karen's mind and body.

No one could figure out what was causing the pain; and no one was trying to find out. The nurses during the day would give pain medicine if she asked for it and at night she would often be given something before she went to bed but it never carried her through the entire night. At three or four in the morning she would often awaken with her arms and hands hurting her so bad she would lie in tears. Luella would be asleep and there were many times that Karen would just suffer it through not wanting to awaken Luella.

The nights became unbearable. The hours of not being able to turn, often burning up in the room and often lying in pain made for long nights of trying to just survive the situation of being uncomfortable to the point of it being sheer torture.

It was a signal to Karen that when the lights were turned out at ten o'clock at night it would likely be seven, eight or even nine o'clock the next morning before she would see anybody. With the exception being of the third shift nurse who would flip on the lights at around midnight, give her the prescribed medication and then flip off the lights and walk back out the door.

9

Do Doctors Ever Come Here?

When we checked Karen into Anglican River, we were told that the nursing home had a staff doctor by the name of Dr. Youngblood. His job was to oversee all of the residents. He had a practice in town but was close to the nursing home we were told. We were asked if we wanted to keep our family physician, Dr. Hank Harley, as Karen's physician, but in the same breath, we were told it would probably be easier to use the staff doctor.

Dr. Harley and his staff had been great to do whatever they could to help Karen but I also knew that he had nursing home obligations at another facility and it would be difficult on him to have to make special trips to Anglican River.

From the outset we were told the doctor did thorough examinations on all the patients every month and was available to see a patient whenever there was any kind of emergency. This sounded fair from the outset.

But looking back, I should have known that in Karen's condition that a doctor's checkup once a month was not going to be enough for her. She had just come from the hospital where a doctor saw her every day. How would a visit from a doctor once a month ever suffice all that she would need? For most nursing home residents a doctor's visit once a month is probably in many cases sufficient.

Admitting Karen into the nursing home became all such a blur to me. The hospital was releasing her and I knew I didn't have the overall stamina to care for her at home. Anglican River had come highly recommended by a couple of people that I respected and so I continued with the hopes that it would work out. The idea of Karen having time to recuperate and have some physical therapy, which the home promoted as a part of their care, sounded appealing.

Dr. Youngblood came to see Karen after she had been in the nursing home about a week. He would prescribe her medications. Most of the prescribed medications would be what she was already taking. Her neurologist in town, Dr. Lad Bilkers, had prescribed most of what Karen was taking. Her drugs included about fifteen different kinds of medications a day.

Dr. Youngblood with his nursing staff did some preliminary customary questions and answers with Karen. It would be the last time he would see her in a caring physician's role. A few days later he would take a vacation and go deer hunting in Kentucky where he would fall out of a tree and break both arms. He would be out of commission and in therapy for the next five months.

A doctor who worked in his building by the name of Dr. Dedi Cope would take over Dr. Youngblood's patients in his private practice and his nursing home responsibilities. I knew from the outset that this did not sound so great. I knew of Dr. Cope and that she had a very excellent reputation as a physician. But I also knew there was such a thing as human limitation. How would she ever see all of her patients and Dr. Youngblood's load of patients? There were a 140 patients at Anglican River. All of these people with the exception of five or six were very elderly and always in need of medical supervision. How would she possibly meet all the demands?

As the weeks would continue I would soon realize that medical care of the nursing home residents was not the top priority. The top priority was to keep everybody fed, out of the way and asleep in bed. It would be scary to find out how many sleeping pills are dispensed in Anglican River and in many other American nursing home facilities. If people are doped and kept quiet then it means less for the nursing home staff to do.

I would also learn that most of the medical care given in nursing homes is done over the telephone. The nursing home nurse calls the doctor's office and talks to a nurse who works for the doctor. The doctor's nurse relays to him what the phone call from the nursing home was about and what is being said about the nursing home resident by the nursing home nurse. The doctor then makes a determination as to how to proceed. His nurse calls the nursing home facility back with the prescribed procedure.

One can only ask how effective this kind of medical care really is? Nursing home nurses are not doctors. They may be very experienced and knowledgeable but they are not doctors. Medical care cannot be given over the phone. I know this because way too many times I have called Dr. Harley and said this is how I'm feeling, maybe I need some penicillin. The response has almost always been, "Maybe you need to come in." I understand that my doctor has to look at my throat, listen to my chest and look into my ears, take my temperature and all of that before he can dispense antibiotics. If this is true for me then why isn't it true for nursing home medical care?

Doctors become very legislated by Medicare and Medicaid. These two federal programs pay the bulk of all nursing home expense in our country. People in America could never afford nursing home care without our federal Medicare and Medicaid program. Yet, these programs have regulations, and there is a limit to how much they are going to pay the primary care physicians. Doctors, understandably, work to be paid. There comes a point where there is a limit as to what they are going to do for any nursing home patient because there is a limit on what they are going to be reimbursed by the Medicare/Medicaid program.

The sad reality is that sickness does not have limits. Sickness will move the body right along the path to death. Sickness does not just decide to stop because the doctor has not treated the problem or because proper medical care has not been given or because Medicare does not cover the cost. When the body reaches a certain point of sickness it will draw its last breath and die.

Karen had two doctor's visits in Anglican River during her six-month stay. Dr. Youngblood saw her near the beginning and then his fill-in doctor saw Karen about a month after Dr. Youngblood had his hunting accident.

Multiple sclerosis is a disease that requires medical treatment. *However, what about the other 139 patients in Anglican River? What was becoming of them? What kind of treatment were they receiving?* These other people surely needed medical supervision as much as Karen.

I had no idea what kind of ramifications such non-medical care would mean for Karen. Her care consisted of daily having nurses give her a handful of pills and a drink of water to wash them down.

Many times I was in the room when the well-meaning nurse would bring Karen's pills into the room. The nurse usually made a big deal about the medicine that Karen was receiving like it was really something special. But all she would be taking was a Prozac, a couple of pills to help with her spasms and a pain pill. The medication was nothing that helped with Karen's declining condition. They weren't medicines that were necessarily beneficial for fighting her disease.

After a couple of months of being in Anglican River I started feeling some of Karen's despair. She had nothing to look forward to. She had to lie awake every day dreading the long nights. While she was awake during the day, she would some days wait until as late as two o'clock in the afternoon to get her morning bath. Soon these baths were relegated to three days a week. If I made a special point of telling the nursing staff I was coming in to take her out by 10:00 in the morning they would give her a bath and dress her for me to pick her up. However, having to bathe and dress Karen this early in the day was real grief for the staff and they hated the fact that I picked Karen up so much and took her out of the nursing home facility.

When Karen began her stay in the facility, the physical therapy department gave her therapy three times a week and then soon the therapy dropped off to nothing more than a speech therapist that faithfully came to work with Karen. We were grateful for the speech therapist that seemed to care and tried to help Karen. However, Karen needed her legs moved, stretched, and manipulated along now with her ever worsening arms. We complained about this to the nurses on several occasions asking for the physical therapy and we were assured it was going to happen; but all we ever saw was a lady who once or twice came into Karen's room and for about three minutes stretched her legs out with Karen sitting in the wheelchair. It was a poor attempt to pacify us. We both shrugged our heads and said, "Why bother?"

I began making special trips to the nursing home to personally work Karen's legs. I knew enough from watching home health care therapists, plus some training they had given me to at least give Karen some relief.

My daily schedule became that of physical therapist to Karen. Every evening I showed up at the facility to make sure her legs were manipulated, stretched and moved in ways to give her some relief. Normally my last acts at night were to brush her teeth: she would go for days without having her teeth brushed if I were not around to do it. The aides could rarely find the time to perform such strenuous acts of care giving. And then after brushing her teeth I would apply Ben Gay to her neck and shoulders. Karen would sit too many hours in her motorized wheelchair during the day and night. She had a headrest but most of the time her head was not positioned correctly against it and her neck would get strained from sitting in the chair. The Ben Gay was always a welcome relief each night.

Normally before I would leave the room, I would clean up a bowel movement that the nursing home staff had not bothered with. Cleaning up other people's bowel movements is not what we really want to do each day. We do it for our babies but we also look forward to the day when they can do it for themselves. It's a little more difficult when we have to do it for an adult. It's one matter when it's for a spouse that we love. I've tried to imagine how difficult it might be if I had to do it for my father or mother. It could happen. We never know what position we are going to be in life.

I've thought about how I would feel if I were Karen and Karen was having to clean up my bowel movements. I would hate it. I would hate anybody that I love having to do that for me. I actually think I could handle some aide or nurse that I did not know very well performing that kind of care on me rather than a loved one or intimate friend.

It didn't take too many trips to the nursing home to soon wonder about Anglican River. *What were these people doing? Where were they? What kind of place did I have Karen in? Why would a place with a nursing staff, aides and a shiny new building be almost totally neglecting the simplest of care for a resident? How much effort did it require to give someone a bath, brush his or her teeth and clean up a bowel movement? How much effort did it take for someone from the physical therapy staff to come to Karen's room and work with her for twenty minutes?*

Anyone who exercises knows a good twenty-minute workout is valuable if a person works hard during those twenty minutes. In Karen's condition, a hard work out didn't require much other than a little attention from somebody to help her.

The total absence of physician care and physical therapy care, the neglect of the nursing home aides and even some of the nurses to provide simple care, would take its toll on Karen.

10

We Have To Do Something— Chemotherapy

From the very beginning of Karen's multiple sclerosis diagnosis, we sought medical help. We traveled to Mayo Clinic in Rochester, Minnesota and saw neurologists in Dayton, Ohio; Lexington, Kentucky; and Evansvelle, Indiana.

Most of the six or seven neurologists who have worked with us didn't seem to know much more than us in treating the disease. I'm not saying they were not capable people. Most of the neurologists were capable, just not with multiple sclerosis. It's hard to be capable with a disease for which there is no cure and every patient's disease displays itself in different ways. However, there are some neurologists who are much more progressive in the treatment of the disease than others. Some doctors are very passive when it comes to medical treatment while others are much more active. Every patient has hopes that his/her physician will be the doctor that will solve and successfully treat their problem.

I was talking to some people in a multiple sclerosis chat room on the Internet about their disease and how it was affecting them. We began to talk about treatments for the disease when one girl from Kentucky told me she was using chemotherapy.

"Chemotherapy?" I typed.

"Yes it's only been approved by the FDA for about a year."

"Has it helped you?"

"Unquestionably. I'm able to get around on a cane now."

"How were you doing before?"

"I was in a wheelchair."

"You feel the chemotherapy got you from a wheelchair to walking on a cane?"

"No doubt about it," she responded.

"Who is your doctor?"

"Dr. Robert Fallis."

This name kind of struck a cord in my mind but I couldn't figure out why.

"Where can I find this guy?"

"He is out of Louisville."

I thanked her and soon signed off the computer. I had never felt good about chemotherapy. It seemed everybody I knew got almost deadly sick from the chemo or had died from using it. They lost their hair and looked like they were walking death. I wondered how worth the chemo treatments were to put a body through such agony.

With Karen's declining health I felt we had nothing to lose. Since her admittance into Anglican River she had debilitated to where her arms and hands had quit functioning with the exception of shaking. The tremors made it impossible for her to hold eating utensils and even operate her motorized wheelchair. The tremors had also gotten into her neck causing her head to shake uncontrollably.

I found the name of Dr. Fallis through telephone directory assistance in Louisville. The appointment was made.

I notified my floor nurse that I would be taking Karen to see a doctor in Louisville. When I showed up, Karen had been bathed and dressed and was ready to go. We made the trip to Louisville where we had our first meeting with the doctor. We had the usual first appointment conversation with him. He told us he would need a new MRI scan or Magnetic Resonance Imaging. He wanted to see for himself exactly what was going on with Karen's disease.

We would go back to Evansville where the MRI would be performed. We would literally pick up the film and take it back to Dr. Fallis a week later.

It would be at this next meeting that Dr. Fallis would give Karen some injections into her neck to try to stop her head from shaking. The injections ended up causing Karen's neck to hurt worse and didn't stop the tremors. For two months I think the injections only ended up adding to Karen's discomfort.

It was in our meetings that I brought up that I had heard that he had used the chemotherapy treatment. He acknowledged that he had and asked if we were interested. We were.

He explained to us that it didn't work for everybody. But that some positive results had been seen in some patients. Karen and I had already discussed it and were ready to proceed.

An appointment was set with an Evansville oncologist.

At our first meeting with the oncologist we learned about the chemo treatment. He had been using chemotherapy for cancer patients for a number of years but never for multiple sclerosis. He was up to date on the procedure, but Karen would be his first patient that he would use chemotherapy for the treatment of MS.

The day came when the date was set for Karen's first treatment. I told her nurse on her floor at Anglican River that I would be picking her up for a chemo treatment.

"You are taking Karen for chemo?" was the way she responded.

"Yes," I replied, "It is a rather new treatment for the disease but some positive results have been seen."

When I showed up at Anglican River I was told by our floor nurse that Nurse Betsy Flossy wanted to see me for a moment. I had no advanced warning of Ms. Flossy wanting to see me and this became a pattern at Anglican River. I never knew when I walked into the building when I was going to be called into the conference room for some questioning or directive information.

"Mr. Mollette, we had no idea you were taking Karen for chemotherapy. That is a very serious procedure. What are you trying to do to your wife?"

I was a little stunned at Flossy's disposition. She acted very unhappy.

I tried to explain to her that chemo was a new treatment for multiple sclerosis and some positive results had been seen.

"Mr. Mollette, whenever you take your wife to anything like this we want to know about it."

"Ms. Flossy, I did call and tell the nurse on Karen's floor that we had this doctor's appointment today. What is the problem?"

I gave Flossy the name of the doctor and told her to call about any special questions and that I was sure his nursing staff would help her with any questions that she had about the treatment.

I told Karen about the inquisition that I had been through when I finally made it back to her room to escort her out to our car. We were relieved to be out of the building and on our way for the first treatment.

When we made it to the oncologist's office, her vital signs were checked by one of the nurses and blood was drawn to determine if everything was okay for her to proceed. Within thirty minutes we were taken to the back of this spacious physician's office where we saw about a dozen other people all hooked up to IV's. They, too, were receiving some kind of treatment and I apprised it was likely chemotherapy. Most of them had the appearance of people that I had seen before who had taken chemo . . . pale and sickly looking.

I dreaded this for Karen. The thought of her losing even a little of her full head of beautiful jet-black hair was appalling. But what were we to do?

The nurse first began a small bag of what she called anti nausea medicine. "This will take about fifteen minutes and hopefully will keep you from getting sick from the chemo," she explained.

Shortly the chemo was started. It was blue.

"Don't freak out later today when your catheter bag is filled with blue urine," she laughed.

"We will try to warn the nurses at Anglican River not to be too freaked out when they change it," we laughed.

Karen was sitting in a very comfortable plush recliner and I sat down in the one next to her. I nodded off for a fifteen minute nap and by the time I had awakened the treatment was about over.

Before leaving the facility we were scheduled to return seven days later when blood would be drawn to check her blood cell count and how her body was responding to the chemo. This would be something we would do for four or five weeks. The oncologist was very good at monitoring Karen's progress.

Within three days, Karen noticed she had some feeling in her feet. She had not felt anything in either of her feet in more than three years. This was awesome! A couple of days later she had feeling in the back part of her legs, calves and hamstring area. She had not had feeling in these sections of her legs in at least two years or more. This was incredible!

Within a couple of weeks after one treatment of the chemo, Karen had feeling in the entire lower part of her body.

Two weeks after this first session with the Evansville oncologist, we were back in Dr. Fallis's office in Louisville. We were elated about how well Karen was doing and wanted to know when we would receive the next treatment.

"The approved recommendation is that the chemo be given every three months for the treatment of multiple sclerosis."

"What? Every three months . . . how could this possibly be?"

"The chemo will continue to work in your body. You will see and feel effects from this treatment for quite awhile. But, if you are seeing this kind of response from the first treatment, then I think you'll be elated when you get the next treatment," expressed Fallis.

The Evansville oncologist explained that each new treatment of the chemotherapy would take Karen to a new level but that it would take about three months for each treatment to do what it could do.

So each day we rejoiced for the new feeling that Karen was feeling in her body.

While further treatments of the chemo could result in hair loss, as far as we could tell, Karen did not lose a single hair from the treatment. Her worse reaction was losing her appetite for certain foods but she still was able to maintain her taste for cherry lime aide drinks and fried cheese sticks from Sonic Drive-In restaurant.

We reported to the nursing staff at Anglican River about how well Karen was feeling from the treatment. We explained that she now had feeling in her lower body and that this would be an excellent time to begin to manipulate her legs and try to see if her muscles would begin to respond some. Our talking about therapy almost became begging for therapy. Occasionally somebody would show up at Karen's room and stretch her legs out, but as far as any exercises—the nursing home did not come through with any.

The only extended manipulation of her legs that Karen received was what I would give to her each night before I brushed her teeth and put Ben Gay on her neck and shoulders. It became terribly discouraging to Karen that she now had this new feeling of some semblance of health that she had not experienced in a very long time but could not build on it with any therapy.

After weeks of asking the administration, the head nurse, Flossy, and even persons from the rehabilitation department of the nursing home, we soon gave up.

Most residents and families of nursing home residents eventually give up. It is very hard to fight passive resistance. The nursing home administration knows they have the winning odds in any conversation or dispute. They have a huge population of families in any community that are looking for care for loved ones. Most of these families will admit the loved one and seldom come around to even see them. These are the kinds of families that nursing home administrations and staffs love. Whenever they have a family like us that is seeking desperately to get well and is asking for their involvement in the process, they are irritated.

Helping somebody to become well requires work. Letting somebody die only requires that the nursing home staff stay out of the person's room and let the process take place. Everybody is going to die. Nobody lives forever. Yet, nursing home residents would live longer and have a better quality of life if they received attention and care.

Neglect kills anything. Neglect your garden and the weeds will overcome it and snuff it out. Neglect your house long enough and the roof will fall in on you. Neglect a frail human body long enough and it will soon whither away.

Unfortunately Karen and I began our process at Anglican River with a misconception. Our misconception was that they tried to help people become better. I will repeat often . . . several of the nurses and aides were great but Anglican River is just another warehouse for frail sick people to be stored out of the way until such time that they die and another frail person is admitted to fill that person's bed. Usually in most nursing homes it doesn't take long to fill a bed and began the process all over again.

11

Care Conferences?

Karen had only been at Anglican River a couple of weeks before I started receiving telephone calls. "Mr. Mollette, this is Roberta and we need to set up a care conference with you." I agreed to meeting with her the next day.

When I showed up at the nursing home I was directed to a room that would become all too familiar. It was called the conference room.

I had a seat and soon several people started showing up. We began the meeting with six of us in attendance. Roberta introduced herself as the social director and then she introduced Betsy Flossy as the head of nursing. The other women in the room sat almost motionless without any introduction.

Roberta began by saying, "We want to go over some things, Mr. Mollette."

I was glad because Karen had been there two weeks and there had not been any orientation to the nursing home. I was finally glad to find out what I could expect from them.

Another lady began talking who was never introduced but said she was involved in nursing. This would be the only time I would see her at Anglican River.

"We are glad that we were able to make arrangements for Karen to be here. Beds are very difficult to come by in this place. We have a tremendous list of people who are waiting to get into this facility."

At this point I did not doubt her statement. The building was clean and was one of the newest facilities in the area. It was very accessible and viewable from one of the main highways. I had not heard anything bad about the facility. Although I had not been investigating nursing homes. This was all very new to me.

The lady continued, "We are glad we were able to work out Karen's roommate, Luella. They seem to be very compatible for each other."

I agreed. Luella was very sweet and was a good roommate. She also had very pleasant daughters and sons who were nice to Karen.

Roberta then spoke up and said, "We want Karen to be happy here. Bring in some of her favorite pictures and put them on the bulletin board or her portion of her dresser. This is her home and we want her to feel good about being here."

This statement was something that I would hear several times later. "This is Karen's home." This sounded strange to me. I didn't feel like this was her home. Her home was with her children and husband. This was not a home I thought to myself. This was some place where Karen could hopefully recuperate and get better. My idea was not to make Anglican River a permanent place. I hoped Karen would be home in a couple of months. After several more weeks of Karen's residency I would soon figure out that few people left Anglican River except in black bags in the back of funeral home hearses.

Karen had a window view of the front entrance of the nursing home facility and almost every day she would tell me, "They took another dead body out of here today. Another black bag was loaded up in a funeral home vehicle. They pulled right up to the front of the building and I watched two men load another dead body and take them away. Is that what I have to look forward to?"

"Not any time soon," I assured her.

In this first care conference it didn't take long before the main issue was introduced.

"Mr. Mollette, from a business perspective you have about thirty days of Medicare and then you will be on your own financially."

The cost of Anglican River was a phenomenal monthly charge. There would be no way that I could afford the first month. This did not count anything else that was tacked onto the costs such as any prescribed therapies, doctor's visits or special medications and on and on. I could see where a nursing home facility could drain the savings account of any senior adult regardless of how much money they had.

I assured them I had been in contact with my local county social services director and that she was working to help us with some arrangements that might make Karen's stay financially feasible.

Roberta then announced, "That's all we have today."

This was the end of the meeting? This was it? This was a care conference? What kind of care conference was this? I would soon discover that care conferences at Anglican River were money conferences and opportunities for the nursing home leadership to place blame for their ineptness on somebody else. No form of conversation ever took place about how to better care for Karen. In later meetings I would become vocal about Karen's care, lack of therapy and inattention. The administrative leadership would sit like zombies as though I wasn't even talking whenever I would breach such subjects as Karen's care.

For the first two months I would abruptly be sought out in the hall as I walked to Karen's room. "Roberta is looking for you. She needs to talk to you." I would end up seeing her and often Nurse Betsy Flossy before leaving the facility. The question was always about what I had heard from my county social services director about the financial arrangements for the nursing home. It became a form of harassment. It became impossible for me to even walk through the hallways of the nursing home without wondering when I would be approached by some nurse saying that the administration needed a care conference. I thought *if I hear this inappropriate terminology used one more time I'm going to croak.*

The day came when the local social services director notified me that Medicare/Medicaid was going to come through. Since the cost of the nursing home facility was more than I made in a salary every month, we qualified for help. When the administration at Anglican River got this word the care conferences ceased. They ceased so much that we never saw or heard from any one in leadership at the nursing home. They didn't need to see us—we were now in the system with the other 140 plus residents. Let's see, this system would pay Anglican River a minimum of $5,000 per month multiplied by the 140 patients who were receiving care. It does not take a genius to figure out that this nursing home like most others could have afforded to hire some aides and nurses. There was no sense in having one aide for sixty-six residents, as had been the case on several nighttime shifts.

After a month or so I would occasionally see Roberta in the hallway and ask, "Roberta, when are we going to have another care conference. I have some questions."

"Oh, we will get around to it," was her response. There was no hurry to meet with me again since the financial pipeline was now in place to their coffers.

One of the players in these care conferences was Betsy Flossy.

Flossy was an interesting character in that she could never bring herself to speak to me when in the nursing home facility. She always looked another way whenever she saw me coming or avoided any kind of personal conversation with me. I felt this was strange. *She was the head of nursing in charge of my wife's care and she couldn't find it in herself to speak to me?* This type of behavior from Flossy went on the entire six months that Karen was a resident in the facility. I never figured it out. Unless Flossy was struck on her self and simply felt she was above the people and patients in the nursing home where she worked.

Yet Flossy wouldn't stop talking in the care conference meetings. Whenever Roberta would call a meeting, Flossy would almost always be present and would have something negative to say.

One of the negatives was that I hadn't told her that I was taking Karen to have the chemotherapy. "Flossy, I didn't know I was supposed to. No one told me I was supposed to tell you. Are you the one here that I should report Karen's every medical move to?"

Another negative that came up in one of the care conferences was that I had been exercising with Karen. Karen had not been getting any therapy and so I took a three-pound weight to the facility and let her lift it with her hands. I thought this type of exercise would be better than nothing. Karen was only at the facility about three months before she lost total use of her arms and hands and soon it wasn't an issue.

The care conferences would eventually become worse and more unpleasant. I eventually figured out Flossy didn't like me. I don't contend to be the world's most likeable person. I'm just a guy who has a sick wife and had hoped maybe that Anglican River could help her and our family some. Unfortunately that is not the mission of nursing homes. Nursing homes warehouse people. They provide a place for sick, frail people to live out their last days so that the healthy family members don't have to be bothered with the frail family member. When family members like myself show up once and twice a day and are taking the resident out two and three times a week then we become an interruption to the home. We are almost a threat to the facility. The family member who comes around daily finds out what is really going on in the nursing home. He or she sees firsthand what kind of real care is going on and no amount of care conferences can cover up the daily neglect of their loved one.

12

A Fever

After being at Anglican River about two months, Karen began to talk about burning up . . . feeling hot all the time. The nurses determined, as they would check her vitals that she was truly running a fever. Karen was soon put on a regimen of Tylenol. Every time her temperature would rise, one of the nurses would bring her Tylenol.

Fever makes anybody feel bad. Whether it is low grade or 103 degrees, fever is bad and zaps any person. It became normal for me whenever I came into the nursing facility to find Karen looking red faced from her temperature. There would be days that her hands felt clammy. I would never turn on the call light asking for a nurse because I knew that it would take forever to get any attention that way. I would end up walking down to the nurses station and say, "My wife is burning up with fever. Could you please give her some Tylenol?" A nurse would come and give Karen the Tylenol.

What became scary was the nighttime when Karen would lie in bed for hours without any attention. Her fever would almost begin to rise around midnight and it would never be until the next morning when the shift changed that she would receive Tylenol for her fever.

It was common for me to go every night to see Karen. Her dread in me leaving the nursing home was that she dreaded the night that was before her. She dreaded lying in bed all night with a fever that seemed to rise throughout the night.

"Glenn, it's just such a miserable feeling to be in bed all night not being able to turn over and burning up."

It was common for me to put Karen to bed and put leg braces on her to keep her legs from completely pulling up to her hips in a fetal position. The braces seemed to help a little as far as giving her some relief in enabling her legs to stay somewhat straightened throughout the night. Yet, I worried because I knew with the temperature she was battling that the leg braces had to make her only that much more uncomfortable.

Before leaving the room I would make sure Karen's nightgown covered her but also make sure she did not have any sheets pulled up over her. "Glenn, I can't stand to have anything on me. When it starts getting hot then at least I know I don't have to battle having cover on me."

Karen was unable to use her hands or arms to pull her sheet down. So if she got covered up with a couple of sheets and the furnace blasted hot air along with a temperature of 101, then she was in for a nightmarish long night.

On many occasions I would get out of bed at five in the morning and drive to Anglican River to check on her condition. The third shift nurse would almost always be sitting at the nurse's station.

"How is my wife doing?"

"She's fine." He would answer. I was in a little while ago and she was sleeping.

He was usually telling the truth in that regard. The third shift nurse would always give her a sleeping pill to put her out if he thought Karen would need him during the night to turn her over. Karen was supposed to be turned every two hours to prevent bedsores.

I would feel of Karen's forehead and discover she felt warm. I would ask about it and the reply would be, "I gave her some Tylenol not too long ago. It should be kicking in."

It's almost impossible to win any arguments or prove negligence. Nurses and aides tell you one thing and then do another. The only way you can know the truth is to be with your loved one almost twenty-four hours a day. If you are going to be with them twenty-four hours a day, then it's easier on you to have them in your home. At least then you don't have to undergo the agony of social workers and administrators who are far more concerned about covering their own skin than they are about providing medical care for your loved one.

I got so tired of asking the nurses and aides to help Karen. Asking for a Tylenol or Advil every time I went into the nursing home got old. *Why didn't they go ahead and do this? Why weren't they taking her temperature and then treating her appropriately? This place had nurses and thermometers why did I have to leave my home at five and six in the morning to see if Karen was burning up from a long night? Why did it have to be that the last action I did at night was to check to make sure Karen had been given something for her fever?* . . . so that she could at least begin her night of rest with some semblance of peace and the ability to sleep a couple of hours before being awakened to fever.

Something causes fever. *Where was the nursing home doctor? Why wasn't the nursing home staff calling the nursing home doctor that we never saw and reporting my wife's fever? Why was the nursing home allowing Karen to lie in fever simply treating her with Tylenol that only brought about a little rest but wasn't curing her?* The fever went on for over four months at Anglican River.

Were they too occupied to find out where this fever was coming from? Were they too understaffed? Or, didn't they care?

One night I came into Anglican River and found that Karen was once again running a temperature. I went out to my car and drove to the nearest convenient store and bought a bottle of Advil.

I came back and gave her two Advil. I thought to myself that at least she might get a break from the fever and be able to get some rest.

I put the Advil bottle beside her bed in her nightstand top drawer . . . totally unhidden and in public view of any aide or nurse who might open her drawer.

13

One Ugly Horrible Bedsore

After being at Anglican River almost two months I was called to an impromptu care conference. This conference was near the end of our grace period. When I say grace period I mean the period of time that our Medicare would cover the costs of Karen's residency at Anglican River.

The pressure was being turned up as I once again sat in the room with Roberta, Betsy Flossy, and a couple of other staff members.

"Mr. Mollette, have you heard anything from social services? What is going to happen with Medicaid? We have not been informed of anything."

"I'm still waiting to hear. I've checked with the department and have been told they are working on all the particulars of our case. That's all I know to tell you."

"Mr. Mollette, the time has started that you will be financially responsible and we wanted you to know that. If Medicaid does come through and picks your case up then it will be okay. They will come back and cover her expenses from three months prior to when you made application. When did you make application?"

"We applied when she was first admitted into the hospital back in October. A lady who has an office at St. Martha's Hospital came up and gave me the paper work to fill out. I was told by her that if Medicaid picked Karen up that she would be covered three months prior to her admission to the hospital."

"Mr. Mollette, we have another concern. Karen has a small bedsore developing on her backside right at the end of her spine near her bottom."

"Okay," I responded. "What is going on with that?"

The nurse continued. It's a pressure sore and we will work to keep her turned in her bed the best that we can. She needs to be turned often to keep her off that spot."

"Karen had one of those once before. When we had home health care Karen developed a sore but after about three months of care it healed up. It was a bad looking sore."

After the care conference I went back to Karen's room and told her about the conference and asked if I could look at her bedsore. I lifted her out of her chair and placed her in bed and rolled her on her side. Her hospital gown moved easily for me to view her sore. There it was . . . a very red open sore. It was about the size of a quarter split down the middle. The openness of the sore made it look like it had to be painful for Karen.

"Sweetie, does this sore on your backside hurt?"

"Not too bad. Sometimes I feel it when I'm rolled on it the right way."

"Karen, are they doing anything for this?"

"No. They say it has to be kept clean and that I need to stay off it."

"Are they helping you to stay off it?"

"Well . . . when you lay in bed all night in the same position, often ten hours at a time, it's hard to stay off it. They almost never come in and turn me at night. During the day when they put me in the wheelchair at eight in the morning, I'm sometimes left there until nine at night. That's a long time to sit in one position."

I was beside myself with this bedsore. I didn't have a clue what to do. I asked one of the head nurses what was being done for the sore. "We are working on it. Those things take a long time to heal."

I knew from when Karen was at home that her last sore had taken awhile. I was pacified by her answer and went back to Karen's room. It is a horrible feeling being stuck with the care of others when you are uncertain they are capable of helping you. It is a further horrible feeling when there is suspicion about the competency of those who are assigned with the task of helping you. And, it is further even worse when you finally figure out that those in charge of helping you could care less whether they do anything to help you or if you are even helped.

I would later be talking to a friend in our community who told me about the success she had with bag balm. She affirmed that it had done wonders for her grandmother. I went to Wal-Mart and found a couple of cans of it.

I took one of them to the nursing home and opened it. I asked Karen if we could give this a try and she was very agreeable to try it.

I put the bag balm on and it looked like any ordinary salve. I later talked to others in the medical profession. They smiled when I told them about the bag balm. Most of them said they didn't think it would help Karen's sore but they didn't think it would hurt the sore to put the balm on it.

I applied the bag balm a couple of times and then one day got a stern message from one of the aides, "Nurse Morton said to tell you by no certain means are you to put any bag balm on that bed sore."

Gee . . . I thought to myself. What are they going to do then? Something has to be done. What is their better plan of action?

The can of bag balm stayed in Karen's bedside nightstand beside the bottle of Advil along with her toothbrush and toothpaste.

A couple of weeks later I would be approached by physical therapy saying they would be working to heal Karen's bedsore. I was glad to hear this.

One day I went into the nursing home and sure enough a lady had the curtain pulled around Karen's bed and said she was putting a dressing on Karen's wound.

I felt good about this. I was glad Karen was getting attention to that area. From that day forward it was my impression that Karen's bandage on her wound was being changed. The head nurse told me that they would be changing the dressing on Karen's wound every six hours. I wasn't at the nursing home facility watching Karen twenty-four hours a day so the staff may have changed and cared for her wound every six hours. I already was aware by Karen's own testimony that she was having horrible nights and that her call light would sometimes be on for hours before an aide would come to see what she needed. Luella had already told me about the number of times that she had to walk down the hall to find a nurse to help Karen out. These reports did not sound good. Truthfully, I should have been already screaming about what was going on at Anglican River. *But who was I to scream to? Who in the world even cared? What was I to do?*

It was at this point that I began to question the sanity of checking my beautiful wife into such a place. I was unsure how well I could care for her at home. I felt it was unfair to ask my two teenagers to spend their every hour at home engulfed in worrying about how every move they made in the house might impact their sick mother. Yet, Karen was a 47-year-old very coherent, intelligent woman who surely deserved better than what she by her own testimony was receiving at Anglican River.

After I put the bag balm on Karen's quarter size bed sore and was scolded by the nurse I would not see the bed sore again. Every time I would see Karen's bottom from this point on it would be covered with a big bandage. Whenever I would take Karen home for lunch or to just spend a few hours out of the nursing home I would not remove the bandage. There was no reason to. As far as I knew, the nursing staff at Anglican River was working on it. The bandage indicated they were doing something to the bedsore.

I would later in a very nightmarish way discover that the "something" Anglican River was doing was worse than appalling. It would resemble something that someone might see in the very worse of horror movies.

Truth is stranger than fiction.

Some of the concocted scary fiction novels on the shelves of America cannot fully compare with the true scary lives that are really lived by real human beings.

Some of these scariest scenes in modern America are lived out in our nursing homes. We think of scary places as being dark alleys, bad neighborhoods and crime scenes that are reported about on television. The real scary place in America is in your local nursing home.

Anglican River would become the place of some of the scariest scenes that Karen and I ever lived through.

What would become hard to fathom was that most of the residents were permanently incarcerated. Nursing homes are not prisons per se. But, they might as well be because there is no escaping them. Most of the time the only way to escape a nursing home is by dying . . . a grim alternative for anyone who would not choose for themselves such an environment of existence of living in a nursing home.

14

Karen Almost Dies

March brought high school spring break. Going anywhere for Jared, Zachary and I had been difficult. It was almost impossible because there was no one to care for Karen. Since Karen was in Anglican River, we decided we would take a three or four day break and go to Gatlinburg, Tennessee. It had been years since I had been to the Smoky Mountains. The boys had never been and so I thought it would be a nice brief break for us.

The thoughts of going on any vacation and leaving Karen behind in the nursing home were torturous to mentally think about. I knew Karen would give anything for us to drag her out of her bed and put her in the car and take her with us.

There had been many times in the past when we had practically done just that. The last Southern Baptist Convention Karen attended was in New Orleans in 1995. She had just started her second year of being dependent on a wheelchair. She was still able to use her legs a little—but very little. Her ability to place any weight on her legs was almost zero. However, she was able to help a little with her body control, as I would work to pick her up out of her wheelchair and place her in our van. Her willingness to travel was admirable. Karen had always loved life and was game to go most any place.

Her greatest joy in life was being with her family and doing anything with her children.

Yet, multiple sclerosis eventually took this pleasure away. Disease cuts us down. Debilitating health of any kind sometimes slowly and other times quickly robs us of life's pleasures. Our pleasures in this life are not really dependent on our financial income. We are duped into thinking our happiness hedges on how much money we have. Some of the most miserable people I know have more money than they can spend. Their money has not brought them happiness. Money helps . . . but it's not the peg that fills the hole of mankind's heart.

In this world there are two keys to happiness. They are:

1. Your relationship to God
2. Your health

Number one is of course the most important because everybody's health will finally fail. Our bodies are not immortal. I believe in immortality and a better life in Christ after death. However, these bodies get old, diseased ridden and die. Our relationship with God is all that is permanent in this life and is all that we are able to carry from this world to the next.

While we are in this world, our health enables us to live our lives and be servants for God and for our fellow man. With good health we can make a contribution to life and others.

What good is a bank full of money if you don't have enough health to draw your own breath? What good are millions if you can't hug the person you love, walk around the block with your children or grandchildren or enjoy common every day tasks?

Take care of your body. God only gives you one body. There are a few repairs we can make to this body throughout life; but the few measures of good health prevention are worth pounds of cure and are invaluable in the dividends that we will reap.

It's important to save and invest money wisely. But if you really had the choice what would you prefer at age 75 . . . a full bank account, but dependence on home health care for your daily hygiene or the ability to care for yourself and work part time if you had to? Nobody wants to have to work part time at age 75 but wouldn't it be great to have the good physical health to do so?

Most of us say *I'll take the good bank account and the good health.* We all do.

But without good health, money isn't enjoyable.

Jared, Zachary and I left to go to Gatlinburg on Sunday morning. We would stop at 7:30 in the morning to say hello to Karen. We would spend twenty minutes with her before leaving. We would tell her how much we would miss her and that we would return Wednesday or Thursday.

Karen sounded croupy. I noticed when she talked that there was the slightest rasp to her voice. She was coughing just a little. It was ever so slight but noticeable.

"Karen you sound like you are croupy. Do you feel bad?"

"Well . . . just the normal fever that I fight all the time."

"Is your throat sore or feel hoarse?"

"Not really. But I do feel like I want to cough more."

"I will tell the nurse out at the station about it. The doctor needs to know about this."

I would kiss and tell Karen goodbye. I walked out into the hallway and found her nurse that would be taking care of her for the day.

"Oh Mr. Mollette," I heard a voice say. "I'm in charge of Karen today. I've never taken care of Karen before. I was wondering if the way she is talking is how she always sounds?"

"Absolutely not," I responded. "I'm glad to see you because I wanted to talk to you before I left the building. There is something going on with her. She sounds croupy. She is coming down with something. Will you please notify the doctor? Will you ask her doctor to check on her? We are going to be gone for about three or four days. I would really feel better if someone would look in on her and check this raspy sound out I hear when she is talking."

"Sure," she responded. "I'll report it to the doctor. We'll take of it." She responded with a smile.

I was glad that I had the opportunity to report Karen's condition to her nurse. I felt better about leaving Anglican River knowing that the nurse who was working Karen's shift could make a note of Karen's condition and report it to the doctor.

The boys and I left to go to Gatlinburg. We toured the shops, walked the streets, went up into the mountains and had as good a time as possible knowing Karen was left behind in her circumstances.

While we were away Karen was lying in a bed with an upper respiratory infection that was slowly strangling her and nobody was doing anything about it.

I called Anglican River on Monday and Tuesday to find out how Karen was doing. Each time the nurse would tell me that Karen sounded congested and that a call had been made to her doctor.

I knew she was sounding congested when we left Evansville; that's why I made a point to speak to the nurse before we left the nursing home.

On Tuesday I could tell that nothing was being done for Karen's condition. I was told the doctor had not been in to see Karen but that the doctor's office had been called. Dr. Youngblood was still out of commission due to his hunting accident and the woman doctor was filling in for him.

As Karen's respiratory infection grew worse nothing medically was happening to improve her situation. On Wednesday morning when I called Anglican River, Nurse Morton told me that an oxygen mask had been placed on Karen's face and that they had been ordered by the doctor to start some antibiotics. It seemed to me that they were four days too late.

The boys and I headed out of Sevierville where we had stayed the night at the Apple Hotel which is right before traffic crosses over into Pigeon Forge. We made the six-hour drive back to Evansville and went immediately to Anglican River Nursing Home.

We found Karen in hot sweat from fever, a breathing mask over her mouth and nose and almost strangling as she was working to cough the phlegm up from her upper chest and out of her throat.

An ICU doctor at St. Martha's had suspicion that Karen's throat muscles were getting weaker due to the progression of the multiple sclerosis. Six months prior in October when Karen was in the facility, the ICU doctor had said she felt they might have to do a feeding tube into Karen's stomach to feed her and a tracheotomy to her throat in order to suction the phlegm out of her throat and upper chest. I knew that was the last thing in the world that Karen wanted.

She had begged me never to take her to the hospital and admit her to an ICU unit where she would be on a respirator. Now she was on one again and had been for three days. I felt miserable just looking at her. I could only imagine in my wildest dreams just how awful Karen was feeling.

Karen escaped death in the ICU unit in October and regained some of her strength back over the next few weeks. I thought when she was released from the hospital to Anglican River Nursing Home that she actually did well the first couple of weeks and even responded well to the therapy. She especially was able to eat, breath and talk on her own. Her vocal chords were off in that her voice volume was so low her roommate Luella had a lot of trouble hearing her. Luella had difficulty hearing anybody . . . but especially Karen with her very low vocal volume ability. The respirator that had been crammed down her throat for the three or four days she was in ICU and had made her vocal chords so raw, that it would require months of work at the hands of the voice therapist to restore her voice volume.

Now Karen was in a situation where she needed all the throat power she could muster and that was coughing up this phlegm; and she couldn't do it.

When we walked back into Anglican River I became a little panicky. I hurriedly walked down the hallway to where Nurse Loretta Jones was working. Loretta had been an incredible nurse to Karen and was always nice to me. I always saw her going full speed trying to help as many of the patients as she possibly could. Her only problem was the same as most of the other nurses—fifty or more patients to see, giving out medications to and medically try to care for. Her job like all the others was impossible.

I approached Loretta and said, "What in the world is going on with Karen?"

She responded with a shake of her head, "She definitely has some bad infection going on. I'm going to monitor her as close as I can tonight."

Wednesday night turned out to be a full night. I let the boys visit with their mother for a few minutes and then drove them home. I skipped church on this evening and went immediately back to Anglican River after making sure the guys had something to eat.

When I returned, Loretta was giving Karen a breathing treatment trying to loosen some of the phlegm in her throat. Karen had a look of panic in her eyes. She couldn't swallow the phlegm and get rid of it nor could she cough it up. It was stuck in her upper chest.

"Glenn," said Loretta, "You can put your hand right here on her chest and feel the phlegm trying to get out. When you and I have anything like this in our chest, we hack really hard and cough it up. She isn't able to do it. She doesn't have the throat power to cough it up."

I tried to console Karen but soon realized that bedside sympathy wasn't what she needed. She needed help. Loretta left the room to tend to other patients and I sat down on her bed and pulled Karen's upper body to an erect position in bed. I had remembered watching a respiratory therapist beat on someone's back and was told this would help loosen secretions such as Karen had and would enable her to gag them up.

I began beating on her back. Off and on for an hour I was holding this fever-ridden woman up in bed, who was in a state of alarm that every breath she took would be her last, pounding her back trying to save her life.

Soon nurse Loretta appeared at the door with a machine that had a long tube attached to it.

"I'm going to try to suction some of that phlegm out of her throat and upper chest."

Within a few minutes Loretta had the machine going and was probing a tube down her throat and neck trying to remove as much secretion as possible. It was fifteen or twenty minutes of Loretta doing all she could to help Karen.

Nurse Loretta probably repeated this process about four times before she left her shift at 1:00 that night—an hour later than she was supposed to.

I would see Loretta out in the hallway in passing and comment, "Karen's throat muscles are so weak. I'm afraid it's the multiple sclerosis moving into her throat and that she is liable to choke to death.

Loretta with a very worried look shook her head and said, "That's what I'm so afraid of and I cannot stand the thoughts of her dying here this way tonight. I couldn't bear to watch it."

Unquestionably, in my mind, Loretta saved Karen's life that night.

Karen seemed to rest a little better in the morning time but by afternoon her fever was skyrocketing again and she was working hard to move the phlegm up out of her throat. The noise in her chest was louder. *Was this pneumonia?* A portable x-ray machine was moved in and pictures were taken of Karen's chest but no pneumonia could be found. I along with Loretta, the aides and other nurses were amazed at this finding.

By early evening Loretta had already made up her mind that she was not going through another night with Karen like she had the previous one and determined that Karen needed to go to the hospital. She called a local ambulance transportation unit that was equipped with some paramedics and monitoring devices and had Karen moved to Deacon's Hospital.

She was taken to the emergency room where for almost three hours she was given a very through going over. Blood was taken, her vitals were checked and the doctor on call determined she definitely had some infection in her body and needed to be on some antibiotics for a few days.

Karen had developed a hate for hospitals. At St. Martha's Hospital on one occasion a nurse tied her one night so that Karen would not interrupt her nap. She had been assigned to care for Karen one night when Karen had been admitted but told Karen she was "exceedingly tired and had to get some sleep and could not be up all night fooling with her."

This was a horrible night for Karen being tied to a bed and unable to do anything for herself. That was one night I sorely regretted leaving Karen in the hospital. But, we think we are leaving our loved ones in the care of compassionate caregivers. Sometimes we are leaving our loved one in the hands of very cruel uncaring people.

Karen's experience such as this one and others made her very paranoid and she wanted to go back to Anglican River. Karen had developed confidence in Loretta and also knew that her roommate Luella was there for her.

The emergency room doctor agreed for her to return to Anglican River but the next night we were right back at Deacon's again as Karen continued to fight the infection. The emergency room doctor put Karen through all the same tests she had been through the night before. This time it was a different doctor. Again it was determined that Karen could either stay at the hospital or be treated at Anglican River. The assessment was that the nursing home could administer antibiotics as well as Deacon's could. So, again Karen was ambulanced back to Anglican River.

The next day Karen was no better and maybe even worse. I entered her room and found she was still on the breathing apparatus and running a fever. At this point I am sick and tired of my wife lying in fever so I open the door to her nightstand and give her some Advil. Nurse Loretta and I agree that she needs to go to the hospital and stay for a while.

Karen is once again ambulanced back to Deacon's Hospital and her assigned doctor this time is a Dr. Bronson.

While we were in the emergency room, Nurse Betsy Flossy from Anglican River called. "Mr. Mollette, this is Betsy. How is Karen doing?" I was appalled at the phone call. This nurse would never speak to me at Anglican River. If she saw me in the hallway she always made it a point to look the other way. She made it clear from her body and facial language that she did not want to have any conversation with me. I found this very odd and unprofessional on her part. She was the head nurse in a facility that was supposed to be caring for my wife. Her salary was being paid mostly by federal Medicare/Medicaid dollars that is paid out of taxpayer's dollars. I was always trying to at least smile and be congenial to anyone I came into contact with at Anglican River. I was clueless about Betsy's behavior toward me.

When she called it almost was a red flag to me. When she asked how Karen was doing and that she hoped the hospital would let her stay it was like she was saying, *I hope the hospital keeps her so we can have her out of Anglican River.* It's possible that Betsy was not trying to say that; but her phone call and sudden conversation with me when she normally would not speak to me was unnerving.

She wanted to know how Karen was doing and I responded that the phlegm and upper chest condition seemed to be the same. I felt like her fever was quieting down but probably it was because I had given her some Advil before Loretta called the ambulance transportation.

Nurse Betsy never heard another word I said.

"You did what?" she was almost shouting.

"I gave her some Advil. She was burning up with fever."

I never in my wildest dreams imagined what would take place after this one phone conversation with Nurse Betsy. She said goodbye and I proceeded back to the room where Dr. Bronson was attending to Karen.

Dr. Bronson in my estimation was amazing in the emergency room. He actually took a couple of hours and worked with Karen. He was in and out of the room and I'm sure tending to other patients but it was obvious that he was tuned in to our situation. He took time to evaluate Karen's scenario, got her going on some IV medication and admitted her to a second floor room.

The care at Deacon's Hospital was incredible. The care was so good that I had hoped they would keep Karen for a month and help her mend back to health.

It was not to happen. Dr. Quinsy, Bronson's partner decided to send Karen back to Anglican River four days later. Dr. Quinsy, an excellent doctor as well, said, "Mr. Mollette, we have no choice. Medicare determines that once a person is beyond danger and the infection is gone that they are to be released. Your wife seems to be doing perfectly fine. Dr. Quinsy was filling in for Dr. Bronson who was off for three days after he had seen Karen in the emergency room.

I hated to hear this because Karen was being so well cared for at Deacon's. It had been so long since she had been in an overnight medical facility that seemed to really try to care for her that we didn't want her to leave so soon. Unfortunately, that's the way medical life is today in America. What Medicare/Medicaid determines or the HMO tells the doctor is in many circumstances the governing rule of authority. As patients we have little choice because we can't afford long-term health care.

15

Nightmarish
Care Conferences

Karen would spend her forty-eight birthday, April 1, at Anglican River. She would be over most of the congestion that had almost taken her life a few days prior. We would celebrate her birthday with cake, balloons, cards and a couple of gifts. Our little party would consist of our immediate family, Luella and any of the nurses who came by for a piece of cake. A bottle of cologne that I purchased for Karen has yet to be opened.

It would only be a few days after this celebration that I was once again ambushed in the hallway of Anglican River. The social worker, Roberta called out my name as I walked past her doorway, "Mr. Mollette, we need to have a care conference."

Once again I entered the facility to have a personal visit with my wife but was, without any warning, ascertained for a meeting.

Whenever I would enter the nursing home facility I would always have to walk past all the administrator's doors in order to proceed down the hallway to Karen's room. It got to a point where I dreaded entering Anglican River. I never knew when out of the blue I was going to be called into the conference room. The conference meetings were always about what the administration wanted. It had mostly been about financial issues but since Medicare/Medicaid said they were going to come through, I had hardly heard anything from any of the administration. I had hoped for a care conference where the actual care of my wife would be discussed. I had hoped that Anglican River would actually start trying to help my wife. So far through our journey all we had seen was Karen debilitate further.

I went into the conference room with three women: Roberta, the social worker; Betsy Flossy, the head nurse; and the administrator, Casey Kongles. I did not know that Casey was the administrator. Betsy Flossy would open the meeting abruptly with a reprimand.

"Mr. Mollette, we have some concerns. One of the concerns we have is the Advil you have been giving your wife. We know that you have been giving her Advil because we found it beside her bed. We know you have been giving it to her because we have questioned Luella her roommate and Luella says that she saw you giving her medicine."

"Mr. Mollette you can't be giving your wife medicine. Advil could cause her to have serious complications."

I couldn't believe this conversation.

The reason Betsy Flossy knew I was giving my wife Advil was because I had told her over the telephone that I had given Karen some Advil.

She was burning up with fever and every night dreaded lying in bed with the lights out burning up in fever.

I was very open in the meeting that there had been a couple of occasions out of desperation for my wife that I did give her Advil for her fever.

Flossy continued, "Mr. Mollette, have you given your wife any other medication?"

"Absolutely not. The only thing I have done for my wife is put some salve on her bottom to try to help the bed sore heal and gave her some Advil for her fever. It would be nice if I didn't have to do those kinds of things. I thought she was here to be cared for. Why would I have to even worry about such tasks?"

Flossy had made her point and Roberta, the social worker, sat and said nothing. Flossy then closed her part of the meeting with saying, "Now our administrator has something to say." And she and Roberta abruptly walked out of the room.

Casey began by saying, "Mr. Mollette, there is another serious matter that we need to deal with. You have seriously hurt someone in this nursing home and I am not going to stand for it." The pitch, volume and intensity of Casey's voice began to rise as she continued her conversation with a sense of almost anger. "In this nursing home we treat everybody with the utmost respect. We do not treat people badly and expect our employees, patients and anyone that comes into this facility to treat everybody with courtesy and respect. What you have done is a bad thing."

It had been a long time since anybody had got in my face and been angry with me. This lady was mad and was ugly.

I was completely dumbfounded.

I sat quietly listening to what was being said to me. As she was bellowing out her words of disdain for my so-called "bad behavior," I could not for the life of me figure out what she was talking about.

"Casey, I began, "I've never met you. This is the first time in all the many months that Karen and I have been in this facility that you and I have ever sat down and talked."

"Well, Mr. Mollette, I am the administrator of this nursing home."

"I see."

I continued, "I had hoped there would be an opportunity to meet you sometime. I've been coming in and out of here for many months now. I kept thinking in all those earlier care conferences we were having that maybe I would meet the person in charge here. I kind of thought Betsy Flossy was in charge. However, you are the administrator . . . is that correct?"

"Mr. Mollette, that is definitely correct. I am not going to have you hurting people here in this facility."

"Ms. Kongles I have to stop you here and ask what are you talking about? Who have I hurt?

"Mr. Mollette, there is a person in this facility that is very hurt. I think it was the way you acted."

I was totally beside myself at this point.

"Ms. Kongles who is this person?"

"Oh I can't tell you who it is."

"Ms. Kongles, I can't go out of this residence not knowing what you are talking about. What you are talking about is something that gravely could affect my work and testimony as a pastor. You are putting me in a position where I will have no choice but to seek legal representation. At least let me meet this person and talk to her."

I had assumed it was a female since most of the employees at the facility were women.

"No, it's not a woman. It's a man."

"Ms. Kongles, I insist on talking to this fellow. I'm not leaving here today until we at least talk."

"Let me go see if he is willing to talk about this."

I waited in the room trying to figure out what all this was about.

Suddenly the door opened and in walked Casey with Mitchell. Mitchell was one of the custodians who worked at Anglican River. We always smiled and said hello in the hallway. We never had any deep personal conversations but we were always nice to each other. He always had a nice smile and was friendly and congenial.

Mitchell looked at me and his face became beat red. "Ms. Kongles, this is not the man I was talking about."

Casey looked at Mitchell and then with her face filled with embarrassment looked at me and said, "Oh Mitchell, I'm so sorry. I thought this was the man you were telling me about. Are you sure this is not him?"

"No, Ms. Kongles, this man is always very nice to me."

I didn't know what to say or do except to smile at Mitchell, shake hands with him and say, "Mitchell, I don't know what this is about but I hope it's resolved."

Administrator Casey Kongles thanked the custodian for coming in . . . told him bye and then extended her hand saying, "Well Glenn, we did it. I'm so glad we talked to that man."

I thought to myself . . . we did it? I had to beg and plead to meet this man. If I had not insisted I would have left the facility with a phenomenal cloud over my head worrying about something that did not even really exist except in the mind of Casey Kongles.

We sat back down at the table and I just broke. I hate crying but this was one time that tears of sheer mental and emotional exhaustion took over. This scene with the nursing home administrator followed by stern reprimands for giving my wife Advil for her fever was pushing me to the limit.

I had already been running on empty. The lack of rest, church responsibilities, teenagers and now pressure from a nursing home that was making my life harder instead of easier was painful.

I took a breath after this encounter with the custodian and simply said, "Casey, I can't believe you have done this. You are a professional woman over fifty years old. You have years of nursing experience. How could you have pulled such a stunt as this?"

Casey wagged her head in agreement. "Mr. Mollette, I do apologize. I made a mistake."

"Casey we all make mistakes. Could you not have pointed me out to Mitchell and asked if I was the man he was talking about? It would have saved him, you and me a lot of embarrassment."

"Glenn, you are right. I made a mistake and I apologized. That's all I can do."

"Casey, why is this the first time that you and I have ever met? I've been coming in and out of here for months."

"Glenn, I had been intending to meet you and talk to you but I just had not gotten around to it."

"Casey, I didn't think I was doing anything wrong by giving Karen an Advil. She was burning up in fever. What would you have done?"

"I would have found a nurse and told her."

"Karen has been battling fever going on five months and the nurses in this facility should not have to be told to check for it and to give medication," I said.

The meeting time was getting long and it had been emotional not only for me but had not turned out the way Casey Kongles had hoped. It would definitely become a bad mistake on her part as a nursing home administrator.

We would adjourn our meeting but I had to go out and think about what had happened to me. It was not over for me. I had been reprimanded even when I had been very honest about the Advil. I was accused of hurting someone. Even though that was now over and gladly everything was okay there was something about being accused of hurting somebody that made me feel like a knife had been thrust through me.

I got into my car and drove for few minutes trying to dissect the so-called care conference. The care conference terminology was appalling. Whenever I thought about walking down the hall and someone calling out my name and saying, *we need to have a care conference,* it made me nauseated.

I would sit down at my desk later that afternoon and type out a response to Casey of which she has on file somewhere I'm sure.

That afternoon I would go back to Anglican River and knock on her door to see Betsy Flossy sitting in her office. I would ask if I should come back later and Casey said it would be fine for us to talk. Flossy asked if I wanted to see her, which I was happy to say no I did not.

I read the three-page letter to Casey. I told her I did not want to mail the letter to her because I wanted her to hear the tone of my voice and know that I was not coming across in anger. I think often letters can be misunderstood. It's difficult to read a letter or email and clearly understand the tone of someone's voice or know the attitude of the heart that produced the letter.

I finished the letter, which addressed my feelings and questions about Anglican River.

A big part of my letter is that I wanted to know what my rights were. Nobody at this nursing home had ever sat down and told me what my rights were as the husband of my wife that was a resident. We were not informed what her rights were nor any of our children.

I wanted to know, "What am I allowed to do? What am I not allowed to do? Is there a piece of paper that says what the requirements of this nursing home facility are? Is there a legal document that tells me what I cannot do to help me wife? My wife is the love of my life. I have cared for her for over twelve years. I have saved her life on three occasions by calling 911 and having her admitted to the emergency room and intensive care units. I want nothing but the best for Karen. But if I am not supposed to do something I want to know about it. If I'm not supposed to give her Advil then where is the documentation that says it's illegal? I'm not stupid. I know all of us cannot give Karen medicine and that it has to be controlled. But I don't want to be called on the carpet for any and every other little thing that I do. Where does it say I'm not supposed to put lotion on my wife? Is there any place that says I'm not supposed to help her brush her teeth? Am I not allowed to feed my wife? What about helping my wife get dressed or brush her hair? What about stretching my wife's legs? She lies in bed for hours with nobody in this facility ever manipulating her legs. Am I out of order when I try to give my wife some relief by stretching her legs and trying to help her be more comfortable? Am I out of hand or doing something illegal if I bring my wife ice cream or fried cheese sticks to eat? All of these questions would have beforehand sounded stupid but I think I need a clear picture of what can and can't be done in this facility."

"Mr. Mollette, we need to have these meetings with families at the beginning of their stay at Anglican River and not after so far into the process. I'm sure it would have helped you and us all if we had been together for this talk prior to today."

16

Anglican River Goes Crazy

A week later after Casey Kongles and I had our heart to heart talk, the fire hit the fan. What I thought had been a very productive talk with the nursing home administrator did not have very lasting results.

A week after our discussion, I called nurse Morton to tell her I wanted to take my wife out of the nursing home facility for a couple of hours. I planned to take her to Sonic or some other drive through. We would likely even go home for a brief break.

Karen loved coming back to her house. What woman or man wouldn't enjoy getting out of the nursing home and returning to the quiet of their home for a couple of hours?

The nursing home is a place of cries and screams for help. It is not a place of refuge and peace.

For Karen, her arms and hands were causing her so much pain she constantly worried about which aide would pull on them in the wrong way causing excruciating pain that would shoot through her like a knife. It seemed she was always having to spend most of her time telling an aide about how bad her arms were hurting her and then begging her to please be gentle with her.

I told Nurse Morton I would pick Karen up right before lunch.

I arrived at Anglican River and unloaded our portable wheelchair. I entered the building and pushed our chair down the hall to Karen's room. I passed Nurse Morton who told me that Betsy Flossy and Roberta wanted to see me. I knew that meant hassle. The only time that Roberta or Flossy wanted to see me was when there was some point they wanted to get across.

I walked down the hall and Roberta was standing there as if she was looking for someone—me. "Mr. Mollette, we need to have a care conference."

I wonder if *care conference* is the only term that some social workers learn in school. Roberta never approached me about us having a meeting or about simply having a talk with me. Her approach was always, *we need to have a care conference.* And then when the conference began it was never about care but about some issue the administration needed to drive home to me.

"Roberta, I'm taking Karen out for lunch and a brief break."

"Oh Mr. Mollette, this will only take a minute I promise. I need to get nurse Betsy Flossy. Wait right here in the conference room."

As soon as I walked into the conference room I turned around and Roberta and Betsy Flossy were coming through the door.

This time Roberta did the talking. It was the first time I had ever heard her talk in a meeting. Normally she always sat over to the side and fumbled with papers when we were having meetings. This time Flossy stood quietly and looked at me with very intense peering eyes. It was as though she was saying, *we are really getting you now.*

Roberta began, "We are not going to let you take Karen out. We have called the prosecutor's office and the deputy prosecutor has given us the okay to forbid you from taking Karen out of this facility."

I stood speechless.

"Tell me again what you just said."

"We don't feel that it is a good idea for you to take Karen out of here," Roberta repeated. If you have any problems or questions about this you can call Janie Cook at the prosecutor's office."

"Karen is going to be crushed. She was looking so forward to having a break from this place today."

Nothing else at this point was said. I was totally numb. *What in the world was going on?*

I went back to the room and told Karen they were forbidding me from taking her out of the facility. She was in disbelief.

I began to gather my thoughts a little after this sneak attack by the nursing home administration. I have never done well under ambush. But who does survive well when two or three in a surprise attack situation jumps them? Anglican River administration had almost made surprise attacks a form of art. I was never told in advance of anything. I was always grabbed at the last minute for a meeting without any preparation to prepare for whatever the discussion was about. That was another problem I was never able to enter the meeting without knowing what was on the agenda. However, that would soon change.

I walked back down the hall and found Roberta sitting behind her desk acting very cocky about her latest accomplishment of being an insensitive social worker with no ability to tactfully communicate or competently work with hurting families.

"Roberta," I began. "May I please have the name of the lady who gave you the permission to do what you just did to our family?"

"Oh sure Mr. Mollette," she said with kind of an arrogant grin, "I'll even give you her phone number."

She gave me the name of Janie Cook, the deputy prosecutor for the county.

I went out to my car and sat as I called Ms. Cook on my cell phone. I got her office and found out it was her day off but was told she could be reached if this were an "emergency matter."

I told the secretary my name and that I would like to be called.

Within five minutes my cell phone rang and it was Janie Cook. "Mr. Mollette, this is Janie Cook and I'm eating lunch but what can I do for you?"

"Ms. Cook, you can tell me what's going on to begin with. What is the deal with me being restrained from taking Karen out of the nursing home?"

"Mr. Mollette, it is possible we can work all this out but could we meet Monday morning? I can meet anytime you want to meet. I can even meet at seven in the morning."

I thought this would be good and agreed to our meeting at seven o'clock. What I didn't know is what I would have to face until the Monday meeting.

I still had not been made clear as to what was really happening.

I went back into the facility and told Karen that I had a meeting with some woman on Monday morning and hopefully we could find out what was going on.

I left Anglican River and went back to work. I had some pastoral visits I needed to make to some other people who were in the hospital.

My next visit to Anglican River would be the next day, which was Saturday. I often would show up at mealtime so that I could help Karen eat her lunch. Most of the aides were good to help but sometimes it's nicer if you know the person that is feeding you.

When I arrived in Karen's room and sat down on the side of her bed, I noticed that within a minute, one of the aides was in our room and sitting down.

At the immediate time I didn't think that much about it. This one aide whose name was Ford often hung around Karen's room. There had been many times when I was visiting that she would come and sit for thirty minutes and say things like, "Just let me sit in here and hide. If I go back down that hall they are going to have me doing all kinds of things."

At other times she would sit and just ramble about one thing and then another. The fact that she had now sat down in our chair and didn't seem to be in any hurry to go anywhere did not seem all that strange.

When Karen's meal came, Ford insisted on feeding her. There was no real reason for me to insist on feeding Karen so I said okay. But Karen insisted that I feed her. At this cue, Ford sat down in a chair directly beside Karen and watched me intently as I gave Karen her every bite.

I had not had a chance to visit with Karen the last few days. We had not had the opportunity to have a private conversation and this aide was starting to get on my nerves just a little bit.

The meal was finished and Ford went back over to the chair at the side of the room and once again resumed her seat.

Soon Ford acted as though she was about to go to sleep and I thought *this is ridiculous*. Two hours passed with Ford sitting in our room. I was on the verge of asking her to leave when suddenly another aide rushed into the room as though she was running late and exclaimed, "I'm here. I'm here." Ford jumped up and ran out of the room as though this different aide had made her late for something. This new aide came into the room and assumed the chair Ford was sitting in. Finally the very slow light bulb in my head began to come on.

I looked at Karen and said, "Honey, we are being watched."

I was in disbelief.

"My word," I exclaimed. "Don't you people in this place have anything else to do but camp out in this room and watch me feed and try to talk to my wife?" I was about to go into shock. This poor girl who had just walked into our room was about to catch the brunt of my irritation. She was just doing what the administration had told her to do. She was likely no more than 22 years old and a very sweet girl.

"Gee wiz," I went on, "What is wrong with you people."

I tromped down the hall and began to stare at the nurses sitting behind the desk and then started demanding some answers.

"What is going on? Why are there sentries stationed in my wife's room? Why am I being watched like a hawk in my wife's room?" The head nurse on duty kind of hum hauled around. The other nurses tried to act busy. Aides were scattering away from the scene. Ford who had been in our room for two hours walked by and I looked at her and said, "You were in there watching me like some kind of guard? Would you mind telling me what is going on?"

About that time, Teresa, who was sitting at the desk, looked around and said, "Would one of you please tell this man what is going on? He has the right to know what is happening."

The older head nurse began to tell me that I was not allowed to be in my wife's room without being watched. The administration had ordered that whenever they saw me go into Karen's room that one of the nurse's or aides were to follow me in and watch my every move. She continued saying that I was allowed to go into the room but not without being observed by someone from Anglican River.

I was in disbelief.

Teresa, who was sitting at the desk, began to tell me about Karen's records. "Mr. Mollette, you need to read Karen's records. They are available and it is your right to be able to access them. I would strongly suggest you read Karen's records."

The records were of course available through the administration's office.

I would later be told from one of the aides that the records of the Anglican River Nursing Home only reported what nurse Betsy Flossy wanted them to report. There were many times, according to one aide, when Nurse Flossy would tell other nurses to omit reports from the records. The aide went on to say if Flossy was telling other nurses to make omissions then what else was being omitted or changed. The records of the nursing home would only record or report what would be in the best favor or interest of the nursing home.

I went back into Karen's room where the replacement aide was sitting.

"Karen, I don't understand what they are doing but I'm going to go home and try to think about this. We obviously will not be able to have any kind of private conversation today."

I kissed Karen and tears were running out of her eyes and down her cheeks.

"Glenn, you need to get me out of here. They are going to kill me."

"We will get you out, but you know I can't do it tonight."

Karen shook her head acknowledging she understood but her face still reflected the pain of what was happening.

Hugging her again I walked out of the room, by the nurses station and out the door to my car.

I went to the house and went to bed on a Saturday night trying to think through about what had happened on this day and was in a state of disbelief.

About ten o'clock, Nurse Teresa called my house and asked how I was doing. Teresa had always been nice and congenial to Karen and I. She on many occasions would stop in the hall to talk to me and ask how I was doing.

"Glenn, I want to encourage you to read the records. They are available to you. I can't say a lot to you because I would be in big trouble if the administration knew I was calling you at home."

"Teresa, I just can't believe this. I still do not understand what is happening. I'll have to find a lawyer to help me."

"Don't get a lawyer. Don't lose your focus."

"My focus? Where should I be focused? My wife and I just both had our rights violated this weekend. My wife is not a legal prisoner of Anglican River Nursing Home. I am not a criminal to be watched like I am a danger to my wife. I have cared for her for over twelve years."

I thanked Teresa for calling but was not in any mood for her to sit on the other end of the line and talk to me like there was supposed to be some logical; sane rational for all that was happening. This was purely crazy and it was the last thing my sick wife needed.

It was bad enough that she was progressively getting worse. It was bad enough that there had not been any physician care given to my wife. It was bad enough that aides and nurses were not available to help her most of the day and night. But now, aides are made available to watch me sit and talk to her? Aides and nurses are available to sit and watch while I feed her lunch? The nursing home doesn't have time to help us but they have the time to harass us? Give me a break!

The next day is Sunday and I go to church and go through the motions of worship. By the time I stand to preach, God has strengthened me and I am able to pull it off. I know that several of my people pray for me and do it consistently. I know that many of my people are friends and listen when I want to talk but don't push me to talk about Karen's illness when I'm not up to it and for that I am grateful. We have a good service. The music, the fellowship and time of worship are invigorating.

I don't know how anyone with illness in his or her family makes it without support. A good church is invaluable.

By Sunday afternoon God has given me peace and renewed my strength. I go back to Anglican River and greet all the nurses and aides with a warm smile. I speak to everybody that I pass and go out of the way to be as nice as possible. I enter into Karen's room knowing that as soon as I do there will be someone behind me. Sure enough as I walk in and give Karen a hug I turn around to see Aide Sandy behind me. This was the one who had been there later on Saturday when I left.

"Wow," I said, "You are still here. Don't you ever get a break?"

She laughed and said, "I am definitely getting my hours in this weekend."

I sat down and told Karen about Sunday morning church and had a little small talk with Karen and then told Sandy, "I didn't mean to leave here in a huff last night but I felt like I had been ambushed."

"Mr. Mollette," she began, "If I were you, I would be as mad as hell. I can't believe the administration of this nursing home is doing this to you." She got on a roll. "My mother has multiple sclerosis and I wouldn't put her in this place for nothing. I'll never put my mother in a nursing home. This place is awful."

I sat stoned face. Thinking to myself, here is an aide that works here and she wouldn't even put her mother in Anglican River. My wife had been there five months. What kind of person did this make me?

Sandy ended up being very interesting to talk to. She was very open.

The day before, Ford had been very guarded about anything she said to me. She was very positive about her work and how Anglican River was the best nursing home she had ever worked for. But I think she was over playing it. There had been times before when she had talked about being overworked and not making any money and having too many patients to care for. She also had talked about being sick and tired of her work on other occasions.

I found Sandy refreshingly honest.

I knew the meeting on Monday morning was coming and there was no way I was going to face the Anglican River administration by myself. Casey, Roberta and Nurse Flossy would look forward to chewing me up and spitting me out. I had to find a lawyer. But who in the world would I find at such short notice and who would come to Anglican River at seven in the morning on a Monday?

17

Attorney Time

I met Attorney David Cell shortly after moving to Evansvelle. His wife was an exercise instructor at a gym where I worked out. His family attended my church and I've been in their home on several occasions.

I emailed David late Saturday night and with a simple message, "I need a lawyer."

By seven o'clock Sunday morning my cell phone was ringing and it was David.

"Glenn, what's this email about?" I proceeded to tell David a little about what was going on at Anglican River and how I had been restrained from taking Karen out of the nursing facility. David was appalled that I was under watch while being in her room.

"Glenn, I have had some experience with nursing homes and the medical industry. Some of these people in those positions think they are God. We will get together briefly after church."

I thanked David for calling and sat down to prepare an account of what had transpired at Anglican River. I would give it to him after church on Sunday morning so that he could familiarize himself with what had been going on.

David and I agreed to meet at 6:20 on Monday morning at his house. We would go together to Anglican River and talk on the way. David had never met Karen and wanted a chance to talk to her before our meeting with the Anglican River administration and deputy prosecutor.

I had a feeling that showing up at the nursing home with an attorney would create a stir and I could feel the glances as we walked into the facility.

I entered Karen's room first and told her I had my friend David Cell and that he was going to represent us at the meeting with the Anglican River administration and prosecutor.

I then brought David into the room and David and Karen talked. He asked her about being restrained against her permission in the nursing home over the weekend and asked her about her feelings about our visits being under supervision. Karen very coherently told David it was totally against her wishes for our visits to be under staff scrutiny. She also wanted to be able to go out for our rides when she and I were able to work it out.

David and I would then proceed to the conference room where the administration staff was gathering. Roberta, Betsy Flossy, Casey and the deputy prosecutor were assembling themselves.

I only nodded my head in acknowledgement of the persons in the room. David and I had agreed that he would do the talking. The deputy prosecutor introduced herself as Janie Cook and I smiled and shook hands with her introducing myself.

David began the meeting with a simple question.

"I would like to know why we are here?"

Casey with a little smile across her face said, "I think Glenn knows why we are here."

She looked at me as though she thought I was going to say something. I said nothing.

David continued, "I believe it would be good for all of us if we had a clear understanding as to why this meeting has been called. I personally have some definite need for clarification about why my clients were restrained from being allowed to leave the premises over the weekend. I also have some concerns with why they were under close surveillance the entire weekend. It sounds like their rights have been gravely violated."

Very little was being said by the administrators.

Casey looked at her cohorts sitting at the table and said, "Maybe we need to dismiss this meeting and obtain our own legal council from the corporation."

"All we are interested in," continued David, "is to clarify any problems that are going on in this nursing home in regards to Glenn and Karen Mollette. There seems to be some problem here that needs to be solved."

Betsy Flossy began to talk, "We are concerned for Karen's safety. We found Advil in her room and were told by her roommate, Luella that she had seen Glenn giving it to her. We have the bottle of Advil in our possession to prove it."

I was in total disbelief at Nurse Flossy. She knew I had given Karen Advil because I had told her over the telephone from Deacon's Hospital that I had given her Advil. There was no need to ask poor Luella and bring her into it. Flossy was acting like she had cared enough about Karen to literally walk down to her room and check her nightstand for the Advil. The truth of the matter was that the only time I had ever seen poor Nurse Flossy in Karen's room was when a local television station came to interview Karen and I and talk about her disease. When the TV station came in, here came old Nurse Flossy bouncing down the hall with the camera crew to our room. When she walked into the room with them I couldn't keep from thinking, *My stars if this woman is a nurse, it looks like to me that she could come down here and check on Karen's health condition sometime instead of waiting until a television crew shows up.*

Flossy continued to make a big deal about finding the Advil bottle in Karen's room.

She then began to talk about another drug called Mysolin that was found in Karen's bloodstream. The level of Mysolin was dangerously high Flossy reported. Finally Flossy and Casey began to get their cards out on the table. The at first subtle accusation was that I had been giving Karen Mysolin. Their thinking was that if I would give her an Advil then surely I would be giving her other medications, too.

I sat in disbelief. This was the first time I had heard about a drug being at a dangerous level in Karen's bloodstream called Mysoline. *Why hadn't I been told? If Karen had been in danger then why had it been kept from me until this meeting?*

"Oh we don't believe Mr. Mollette would be giving Karen anything to intentionally hurt her. We are sure he would be giving it to her thinking that he was helping his wife just like with the Advil," said Casey.

I leaned over and whispered to David, "Where am I supposed to be getting this drug?"

David voiced my good point stating, "Can my client walk up to any pharmacy and just demand this drug? Doesn't it require a physician's prescription?" The administration had no response.

This first meeting with the administration was very brief. The deputy prosecutor said she wanted to talk privately with Attorney Cell and if possible she wanted Karen's doctor present in our next meeting.

Before the meeting was over, David insisted that the prosecutor Janie Cook release her order restraining me from taking Karen out of the nursing home for lunch or a ride in the car and further that all sentries be ordered out of the room when I was in to see my wife.

Prosecutor Cook looked at Casey, Flossy and Roberta and said, "I have no reasoning to keep this couple restrained in any way without some further better reasoning than has been presented here today."

Kongles began to shake her head in dismay and Flossy crossed her arms as though she had been slapped. Roberta the poor social worker sat without saying a word. She was speechless throughout the entire meeting.

David continued, "Okay we are done. My clients will resume their normal activity and we are finished here today."

"We will want to get together one more time," declared Cook. "I do want to hear what the doctor has to say."

David and I got up and walked out of the room. I walked down the hall and told Nurse Morton that in about two hours I would like to take Karen out for lunch if it would be possible.

"Sure, Mr. Mollette, we will see to it that she is ready."

Nurse Morton had always been excellent to us but worked for Anglican River and had to follow nursing home protocol. She would of course check with Nurse Flossy to make sure she was permitted to proceed with dressing my wife to go out for lunch.

I would take David back home and we would briefly talk about our next meeting.

"David, aren't you glad you went to law school?"

"Today I am. I felt like I helped somebody today. Most of the time, Glenn, I just deal with money. It's really good to be able to help somebody."

"David, Karen and I can't tell you how much we appreciate you."

Two hours later I showed back up at Anglican River to take Karen out to lunch. The nurses and aides were much nicer this time. It is truly amazing how the appearance of the law has a way of changing people's dispositions.

I'm afraid way too many people are pushed, shoved, screamed at and literally abused in nursing homes and they will never be able to call a lawyer in to help them. So often the family has seen them sick so long that they simply walk away from the nursing home facility with their heads down allowing their poor loved one to endure the abuse of a calloused nursing home administration and a ruthless money hungry corporation.

I would take Karen out that day for a couple of hours. It had been the first time she had been out in our family car and away from the hospital/nursing home environment in many weeks.

"Glenn, it feels so great to get out of that place. I don't know how much longer I can take it."

I knew I had to figure out something. Our relationship with Anglican River had unfortunately gone south. Sadly, I didn't know why. The most puzzling mystery to me this day is why Anglican River went sour. All I did was go see my wife every day and tried to make sure she was cared for in a humane way. I tried to show her love and care by helping her as her husband but also as a person who had cared for her for over twelve years.

Possibly, this was part of the problem. Being around the nursing home every day is not what nursing homes honestly like. Many staffs would just as soon to be able to sedate the resident and keep him/her sleeping most of the day and night. If a resident is drugged, as many are at Anglican River, then they require very little. They can push them into a cold shower three times a week, which happened regularly at Anglican River, rinse them off, put a robe on them and put them back to bed. It doesn't matter if they die because there is an endless population of American people standing in line waiting their turn to be admitted by families who cannot care for them. Or, do not want to be bothered with them.

American nursing homes are people warehouses with an unlimited supply of people to warehouse before they move from this life to the next.

18

The Final Meeting

After the meeting with the nursing home administration and the deputy prosecutor, David would talk by phone with the prosecutor and learn more.

Calling me at my house, David began to fill me in.

"Glenn, I talked with Janie. She told me that thirty minutes before you came to take Karen out of the nursing home that Betsy Flossy called her and said that you were coming to the nursing home to pick Karen up and take her out for an assisted suicide."

"Do what David?"

"Yeah, that's right, the nursing home called the prosecutor's office and told them you were coming to pick Karen up to do an assisted suicide."

"Are those people crazy? I was picking Karen up to take her for a ride and probably lunch somewhere. I've been doing that a couple of times a week or more ever since she has been at Anglican River. What made them come up with that theory?"

David continued, "The nurse at the nursing home determined that since you give Karen some Advil that probably you were trying to kill her."

"David this is the most insane craziness that I've ever heard of. I think they are just trying to turn the tables on me. The truth of the matter is that they don't want me to do anything for Karen. They want Karen to lie in her bed all day in a bowel movement and feed her whenever they take a notion. David, it's almost seven o'clock some nights when they finally bring Karen her dinner and then a lot of nights it's not been more than a sandwich."

"The prosecutor said that Flossy called and said you were there to help your wife kill herself and asked, 'What was she to do?' She had no choice but to ask that you not take her out of the nursing home until Monday when she would have a chance to talk to everybody. She wants to have another meeting as soon as possible to clear this up."

In the meantime going to Anglican River felt strained. Every time I walked through the hallway I could feel tension. While the nursing staff was helpful and congenial, I could feel the pressure from all the talk that was going on in the facility.

Luella had a son about forty-eight years old who was funny as a monkey. There was never a night that he wasn't trying to crack a joke when he was visiting his mother and talking to Karen. Whenever Karen had company it was like Luella had company, too, and the same for Karen whenever Luella had company. Everybody seemed to share in the conversation.

"Glenn, they really love you here at this nursing home."

"Jack, I know. They hate it when I leave at night. It breaks their hearts."

Jack giggled, "Well, I think it's good that you have them stirred up a little. Sometimes a person has to raise a little cane to get things done."

"Jack truthfully, I don't know what their problem is. I gave Karen an Advil a couple of times but she has been dealing with this crazy fever. I don't understand why they don't ask the house physician to find out what is causing this fever. There has to be some reason for this. They've been dishing out Tylenol to her for almost four or five months now. She started running this fever almost constantly after she had been in here for a month or so."

It's always easier to put pieces together in hindsight. It would later seem that Karen's fever began about the same time of her bedsore.

The next day I would receive a call from Attorney David Cell. "Glenn, they want to have a meeting with us in one hour."

"One hour? They are really giving us a lot of notice."

"Dr. Youngblood is in the building and they want to have the meeting while he is present and can attend. They also want Karen to attend. Do you have any problem with Karen attending the meeting?"

"No, I don't have a problem with her attending but I wonder if this won't be hard on her emotionally. She will be okay but I hate for her to be put through this."

I would pick David up at his house and we talked on our way to the nursing home.

We would go to Karen's room where David briefly chatted with Karen and then he left to go to the conference room where Dr. Youngblood, the nursing home administration, and Janie Cook, the assistant prosecutor were waiting. The local ombudsman would join us for this meeting, Lilly Homer. I would assist Karen in her wheelchair to the conference room.

The prosecutor took the lead in the meeting and said, "Let's get this going and dealt with." She looked at the administrators and said, "We need to put the cards on the table. You folks believe that Mr. Mollette was here the other day to help with an assisted suicide. Is that not true?"

Sheepishly Casey, Flossy and Roberta kind of hung their heads and with blushing faces somewhat acknowledged what Janie was saying.

Looking at Karen, Janie asked, "Were you and your husband planning a suicide?

"No," stated Karen emphatically.

"Has he ever given you anything other than Advil while you have been here?

"No," answered Karen again very emphatically.

Flossy couldn't stand it any longer and began to get into the conversation.

"The blood tests from when Karen was in the hospital showed her mysolin level was dangerously high. We feel Mr. Mollette was giving her Mysolin. If he would give her Advil then he would give her anything else."

At this point I reminded David that Advil could be bought over the counter but that Mysolin was a prescription drug. If I were giving Karen prescription drugs then where was I getting them?

Janie then asked Dr. Youngblood if he believed that Karen had to go to the hospital because of an attempted overdose?

"No," he began, "There is no reason to suspicion Mr. or Mrs. Mollette did anything wrong. It could very well be that her body is not metabolizing the drug. The nursing home is giving it to her three times a day. It may be that because of the chemotherapy the level of the drug has stayed up. There could be a lot of reasons."

At this point, Casey and Flossy tried to pull their last card.

Casey began, "Let's ask Mr. Mollette to stay away from Anglican River for two weeks and then let's see if the mysolin level in Karen's bloodstream goes down."

I looked at Karen in disbelief.

Flossy chimed in, "If the mysolin level goes down then we will know that Mr. Mollette was giving it to her."

By this time poor Dr. Youngblood was shaking his head. It was obvious that he was in shock at the rational and behavior of this nursing home administration and staff leadership.

"What do you think about that suggestion, Doctor?" asked Janie.

"I can't see any real reason for doing that," he responded. "Especially since this is a first time incident. Plus if anything suspicious had been going on with Karen, the emergency room personnel would have been right on top of it. Those people are really good at detecting suicide attempts."

Casey then grasping for straws blurted out, "Well if Mr. Mollette feels he wants to treat Karen, then he can take her home!"

David said, "We'll let you know."

Karen was all for coming home as immediately as possible. "Glenn, I'm ready. Take me home."

"Karen I need to make some arrangements. Give me some time."

At this moment Lilly Homer, the Ombudsman, spoke up and said, "I'm here to be an advocate for the family. If there are problems that the family is having then it is my job to take their side. And, I shouldn't say anything in support of the nursing home." At this point my attorney blurted out, "Then don't. Why would you speak in behalf of the nursing home if it is your job to work in behalf of the family?"

Ombudsmen are paid to work on behalf of the family when they have concerns or problems with how their loved one is being treated. Unfortunately, administrations cuddle too close to ombudsmen, taking them to lunch and becoming buddies with them. It is questionable how helpful the average ombudsman is to the family. Their usual solution to helping a family is finding the loved one another residence to move to.

Janie looked around the room and said, "I see no reason to continue these conversations." She looked at the nursing home administration that now had their heads down. "Without some official word from the doctor I cannot keep this husband and wife away from each other or separate him from visiting her in this facility or taking her out for rides and lunch."

At this time Karen spoke up and reminded the group that she was a fully coherent person who would make her own decisions about what she did and was not a prisoner to any nursing home. Dr. Youngblood, the prosecutor and my attorney all shook their heads in agreement with Karen.

At this moment my attorney jumped up and said, "We are done and we are out of here. My clients will resume their lives."

After the meeting David, Dr. Youngblood and the prosecutor would all talk in the hallway and agree that they had never seen anything quite like this from a nursing home administration.

Dr. Youngblood said, "I've been around a lot of scenarios but this is the first of anything like this."

I would take Karen out to our van and load her into the passenger side in the front. David would get in the back and the three of us would go back to his house where we simply talked about our relief that the meeting was over and hopefully we could have some peace at Anglican River.

"Glenn, I don't know how much peace you are going to have there. They obviously want you out of there. I don't know what the problem is . . . maybe it's a personality clash but Flossy and Casey definitely don't like you and I think they will do whatever it takes to run you and Karen out of that nursing home. I would be thinking about some other arrangements."

I asked David what I owed him for his legal services. He thought briefly and knowing that I am a University of Kentucky basketball fan, said, "You owe me singing the Indiana University fight song three times."

We laughed.

"David, I don't know that song."

"Learn it," he laughed.

Karen and I would spend most of the afternoon out of the nursing home facility and in dread of going back yet grateful we seemingly had a break from the sentries and pressure from the nursing home administration.

19

Leaving Anglican River

Within only a couple of days of our final meeting with the deputy prosecutor, our attorney and nursing home administrators, my phones began to ring. Phones is what I meant to say. The nursing home had my office number and cell phone along with my home number. I started receiving calls asking, "Mr. Mollette, what are your plans for Karen?" Or, "Mr. Mollette, your wife is not happy here; why don't you find some place else for her?" Or, "Are you looking for some place else for your wife? Are you going to take her home?" The harassment from this nursing home administration was appalling. Did the corporation know about this? Is this the way the owners of this nursing home treated every family?

Sally, who was another social worker at the nursing home, was making most of the calls. Roberta never called or asked to have another care conference with me again. Casey or Nurse Flossy never spoke to me again.

It was as if they felt like they had to be in total control of our lives.

Social workers feel like their calling in life is to interfere in the lives of couples and families. To some extent they don't have a job if they are not messing in somebody else's life.

Months earlier a social worker from St. Martha's Hospital had visited our home almost every week. Her mission was to completely revamp our home. Her intentions were good. She was doing her job. However, there was no way we could do everything she thought we could do even though her recommendations were good. In time her suggestions such as widening all the doorways in the house, installing a system that would automatically open the front door of our house and many other ideas were all practical suggestions. My priority list at the time just happened to be figuring out how I was going to be able to keep Karen cared for while I did my work and kept my kids cared for.

I continued to visit Karen every day at Anglican River and Karen began to press me to get her out.

"Glenn, things are getting worse here. It's so obvious by the way they are with me that they don't want me."

"Are they hurting you?"

"The worst is when they pick me up. They know my arms hurt, and the aides have almost made a point of pulling my arms off. They come to the room to turn me over just so they can grab hold of my arms, twist them and make me cry. Every time they leave the room I am in excruciating pain, crying, trying to get over them pulling on my arms so hard. They could be much more gentle when they move me."

"Plus, it's their attitude. It's the expression in their faces. They are so slow about helping me do anything if I really need them. I lie for hours with this fever. A couple of the aides are more distant than they've ever been. I feel totally uncomfortable with some of these people now."

"Okay, we'll see what we can do. I have to at least arrange for home health care."

The last time Sally had called I had said, "Sally, please give me a couple of weeks. I can't just yank Karen out of there and bring her home. I'm not ready at home for her physical care yet. Please give me some time." Sally had agreed that she would stay off my back for a little while.

The next time she called I said, "Let's try a group called Home Health Nurses."

"Okay, I'll be glad to call them for you."

The next day an admissions counselor for Home Health Nurses was at my wife's bedside evaluating her for admission to their program. We had home health care before so we were very familiar with the process. We knew we would have an aide that would help Karen take a bath three times a week and nurses who would come to check Karen's vitals. I also knew that since Anglican River had been treating Karen's bedsore that there was some obvious work involved in taking care of the sore.

The assessment was made and the Home Health Nurse group accepted Karen. It would be up to us to call them when it was time for them to start coming to our home.

By the middle of the week Karen was ready to come home. I had planned to wait until after the following weekend because of some scheduled events I wanted to handle first.

On Thursday Karen said, "Glenn, please don't make me endure another weekend in this place. There is no way I can live through another weekend in here. They are killing me."

The weekend neglect was worse sometimes than what she had gone through on the third shift. Mainly the problem was understaffing. One nurse would be caring for fifty patients or more. Or, one aide would be caring for fifty or more patients.

The neglect of the patients was unbelievable. Again, when corporations and administrations do not hire enough aides to do the job the patients are going to be neglected. A large corporation that has nursing homes everywhere owns Anglican River Nursing Home. Chances are you may have a loved one in one of their nursing homes. What are they doing to your loved one? Are they sedating them into complete numbness? Are they allowing a bedsore to develop on their bottom? Are they feeding them? Is your loved one losing weight because they cannot really feed themselves and therefore she/he is not fed? Aides don't take the time because they don't have the time to see that the patient adequately eats. Are they so understaffed that your loved one lies with his/her call light on for hours in pain? Are they being allowed to live and lie in fever for weeks and months without a physician's attention? Your loved one is probably enduring these and many other discomforts while the corporation owners and administration is living it up on the huge executive salaries they draw from the Medicare/Medicaid dollars pumped into the nursing home facility.

I made the call to Sally that we would bring Karen home the next day. She said she would have the mobile unit there by noon to pick her up and deliver her to our house. I assured Sally I would be at the nursing home by mid morning to pick up Karen's clothes and other personal items.

When I arrived, there were three aides taping up the last of several boxes of personal items and clothes that Karen had accumulated at the nursing home. I had never seen anything like this in my life. These aides were doing more than I had ever seen them do before. Everything that Karen owned was stuck on a cart and before I could blink my eyes they had all of her boxes at the front door ready to be loaded in the mobile unit. It would not have surprised me if they had set them on the street. For days I tried to make sense of some of the boxes. I could not believe how Karen's personal things had just been dumped into some boxes as though they were being thrown out to trash.

For weeks I sorted through the boxes trying to locate personal items that Karen needed for daily use.

The mobile unit arrived and the gentleman helped Karen motorize her wheelchair onto his wheelchair transportation unit. A couple of the aides helped me load the boxes into my van and we were out of there.

It was like we were leaving a bad dream. It was as though we were driving away from the city of horrors. I knew that caring for Karen at home would be tough but in no way would match the pressure of having to deal with nursing home administrators, social workers and a facility that was poorly understaffed to do the work.

20

Dear God . . .
What Is This?

Karen would arrive home and exclaim as the mobile driver shut the door behind her, "I am in my home!" She was truly celebrating. I felt great about her being home and rejoiced with her for this good moment. It was a feeling of immense relief to be out of Anglican River.

I loaded Karen up into our van and we headed out for some lunch. She was going to join me in my church study for a couple of hours while I did some work on a couple of projects. I had just received the rough drawing for my second book, *Spiritual Chocolate,* and wanted to pull it up on the computer to show Karen.

"Glenn, that cover is beautiful."

"Yes," I replied, "The girl who drew this is a really good artist."

Karen was at complete rest in my study as I spent some time making notes and going over some projects that I was trying to complete.

When we returned home Karen wanted me to put her to bed.

"Glenn, if you'll put me in bed I'll sleep awhile. Also, I want you to take that gauze off that sore on my back. They have kept it completely bandaged the entire time I have been at Anglican River."

Putting Karen to bed I turned her over on her side and began to remove the bandage. I had not seen the bed sore for two or three months.

"Dear God . . . What is this?" The question was a serious question to God and not slang terminology. "Uh . . . Karen, this bedsore is bad. Honey, it's real bad."

For a moment I froze. The next moment I was terribly upset. How could a nursing home send my wife out the door with a bedsore that was larger in diameter than any large drinking mug I drink coffee from and so deep that it looked like I could see her tail bone. How could anyone do this to my wife!

The wound was literally black and runny and the smell was horrible.

I didn't know what to do. The nursing home never one time gave me one minute of instruction as to how to treat this wound. There were no instructions on what to do when I got Karen home. They literally pushed us out the door without any care about the welfare of my wife's life. This wound was life threatening. Looking at this wound, one thought rolled over in my mind, *something like this could kill somebody!*

I knew that a nurse from home health would be at our house the next day. A part of her job was to help care for this wound. I was at a total loss. I was clueless on what to do with something this big. Her backside at the bottom of her spine looked like someone had attached a hand grenade and set it off literally ripping out a phenomenal crevice of her body.

"Karen, does this place on your backside not hurt?"

"No, I really don't feel that much back there. If someone probes on it I can feel pressure but there is very little pain."

I would later learn that most bedsores get worse because once they break the skin the patient feels very little and that's why it's so easy for them to get larger and deeper until they become almost impossible to heal.

I would also learn that neglect plays a serious factor in the beginning and continuation of bedsores. Nursing homes are apparently notorious for bedsores. Patients who are invalids require extreme attention in being turned over and repositioned in bed. Any resident allowed to sit all day or lie in the same position for hours at a time will develop little red spots that will become bigger and soon break through the skin. This skin break will only become bigger and deeper as pressure is continued on the sore. For this reason the patient needs to be off the sore as much as possible.

Nursing homes who are understaffed do not have the personnel required to keep the patients turned. Karen was supposed to be turned or repositioned in her bed every two hours. For most of her many nights at Anglican River she was never turned. During the day she was left for hours in the same position or stationed in her chair for hours.

From the outset of Karen's initial residency we had asked she be permitted to stay in her motorized chair much of the day. Unfortunately as this bedsore developed and got worse, no one said to us, "Karen needs to be off that pressure sore. And she needs to be repositioned often so that it will not become worse."

As I stared at this huge crevice at the bottom of Karen's backside I tried to think about what to do.

We would try to get through the night and wait until the next morning when the home health care nurse would hopefully help us. I got my camera out and took some pictures. Nobody would ever believe me if I tried to tell them that my wife had a cave on her backside. The pictures taken on the very day of my wife's release from Anglican River would vividly show what Anglican River allowed to develop. It would also unfortunately show the very extreme extent to which she was neglected. Further it would show the incompetency of the facility.

Health officials would later tell me that a bedsore the size of Karen's could take eight months of longer to heal. My initial reaction was that Anglican River had six months and gave her a bedsore. Every day I thought somebody was treating Karen's wound. Why had it not healed with six months of professional care? On the other hand why was it allowed to ever get to the proportion that it had reached?

The next day the health care nurse came and looked at the sore. She had trouble hiding her feelings of aghast. She took pictures as well for Karen's file and then showed me how to dress the wound. Tedious would be an understatement. In all my days of care giving, dressing a wound the size and seriousness of Karen's would be nothing like of which I had ever dealt.

The bandage would have to be changed twice a day. Gauze soaked in solution would have to be installed. Medication was ordered to apply inside the wound. Putting on the gloves and going through the ritual to prevent infection was a first for me. This was going to be tough.

On Saturday, Sunday, Monday and Tuesday nurses came and went through the process with me of changing this bandage. They were mostly doing the changes but leading me through the process. I was amazed at how good these nurses could make these bandages look.

During these days I would learn from home health care about the extreme importance of nutrition. Karen's body was losing vital protein and nutrients through this wound. The puss like substance that was running out of this wound was valuable protein that her body needed to aid in the healing process.

I began feeding Karen protein bars like crazy. I started trying to get an extra seventy or even hundred grams of protein down her on top of what she was eating . . . which wasn't a whole lot. Karen's weight was down to about a hundred and four, which was low for a 5'4" woman. Karen needed to weigh 120, especially since she was trying to fight a bedsore. A skinny body only seems to make a person more vulnerable to bed wounds.

I had wondered about Karen's daily nutrition while at Anglican River. I had seen her evening meals and had not been very impressed with the substance of the food. Her lunches had appeared decent but the one good meal a day was not enough to combat all that she was losing nutritionally through her wound. Her breakfast consisted maybe of some juice and toast.

Karen has never been a big eater and while I know the cook at Anglican River would have fed Karen anything she had wanted I have to feel that the administration failed to oversee her diet. The head of nursing surely knew that nutrition played a vital role in the healing of such wounds. Why Karen's protein intake and daily meals were not closely observed is beyond me. Again, neglect and the lack of real supervision had to play a vital part in the development of such a wound.

On the fourth day of Karen being home from Anglican River I was able to get Karen to eat three protein bars with each having over 20 grams of protein. She also ate a loaded sweet potato with brown sugar and butter and large protein shake with protein powder and peanut butter added. I felt really good about how Karen was trying to eat some additional supplements.

I put Karen to bed and began the process of giving her the nightly regiment of medications which mostly included a few pills for pain, muscle spasms and the injection of Copaxone a drug used by multiple sclerosis patients. I gave Karen a couple of Tylenol to help her with her low grade fever that she was running and had run now for several months. I kissed her goodnight and told her I loved her.

At four in the morning I awakened and got up to roll Karen over on her opposite side when I detected her breathing differently. I had seen Karen this way before. There had been other occasions in the past when Karen had taken five pills instead of two pills and it would put her into deeper slumber. Karen's look and breathing reminded me of those times but I knew she had not taken too many pills. I had given her the precise dosage as called for on the medicine bottles. Wondering what was going on I could only determine that she was having some time of reaction to the medicine and that she would likely have to sleep it off. I was wrong.

By eight the next morning Karen was still sleeping but not comfortably. I tried to wake her and Karen's speech was slurred and she was only able to mumble, "Glenn, something is wrong . . . I'm having trouble." I went to call our home health group but our phone was already ringing and it was a nurse named Sunny.

"Mr. Mollette, I'm supposed to come by and help with Karen's wound bandage and was wondering if right now would be a good time."

"Please come immediately if you can. Karen is having trouble. I'm not sure what is going on. Maybe she is having a reaction to the medication."

"Okay, I'll be right there."

Within thirty minutes Sunny was coming into our house and getting her medical supplies out. The first thing she did was to take Karen's temperature.

"Oh no . . ." She was startled. "Her temperature is 104.9! Glenn we have to get this woman to the hospital."

I knew Karen had felt warm but she had felt warm for months.

Karen was waking a little and was semi coherent.

"No . . . I don't want to go to the hospital. I'm sick of hospitals."

Sunny took charge. "Karen you have to go. You could die today if we don't get you to the hospital. This is critical."

"Glenn, call 911."

While Sunny was talking she was examining Karen's wound and began to get infuriated. Letting out a few choice words and infuriated she said, "Glenn, where has your wife been to get something like this on her backside?"

"Anglican River."

"This woman needs critical care. Anglican River is not a critical care facility. They didn't have any business trying to care for someone like this. I can't believe they even admitted her as a patient. They are primarily just an assisted living kind of place. This woman is sick."

"Where is that emergency squad!?"

I called 911 again and was assured by the operator that the medical team should be there in just a moment.

Finally they arrived and loaded Karen up on the cart and took her out to the emergency unit vehicle.

"Glenn, she needs to be in an acute care facility. Put her in Safe Care at Deacon's Hospital. I work there a day or two a week. They deal with people like your wife all the time."

I appreciated Sunny's recommendation and thanked her for helping us.

I got in my car and arrived at Deacon's Hospital right behind the medical emergency unit.

Our doctor before had been Dr. Bronson and we asked if he could be called to see Karen.

Dr. Bronson is a doctor employed by the hospital. Apparently many hospitals are going to staff doctors who treat only in-house patients and do not maintain an outside office where they take daily appointments.

Dr. Bronson would begin the examination trying to determine what was causing all this fever and also first of all, trying to bring it down before it did some kind of permanent damage to Karen.

21

Good Doctors
And Good Hospitals
Make All The Difference

Dr. Bronson and his team of other hospital doctors and nurses worked on Karen for three hours in the emergency room of Deacon's Hospital to bring down her fever and stabilize her. Many vials of blood were drawn, x-rays were taken and everything about her was examined including the very appalling wound.

She was admitted; and by the next day, Dr. Bronson and his medical team decided that Karen had a staph infection. A very serious infection that had apparently gotten into her blood stream sometime Tuesday night when she started showing signs of being in trouble. It could have killed her and would still kill her if not gotten under control.

Karen was doused with antibiotics to begin to ward off the progressive staph infection and stabilize her life.

Where did this infection come from?

It was almost conclusive that the staph infection had developed as a resort of the horrible wound. Her tailbone showed several spots of the staph infection that would have to be removed by cutting off part of Karen's tailbone. The sore could not be allowed to heal over this staph infection showing up on her tailbone. It would only cause her trouble as it was doing now.

The phenomenal care that Karen received for several weeks by Dr. Bronson and the fourth floor staff at Deacon's Hospital was like an oasis in a long dry dusty desert for us. This doctor really seemed to care and was constantly in and out of Karen's room trying to make her life a little better and easier.

His willingness to be thorough and work to bring about some semblance of better health for her is appreciated more than mere words can communicate on the written page.

A hospital staff that cares and tries is invaluable to the patient and the family that is struggling to deal with illness.

The dousing of Karen's body with the antibiotics took about a week before Karen's fever was staying at normal. For days it was an uphill battle of 102 and 103 degrees temperature. Finally the antibiotics seemly took control and Karen' s body temperature began to stay at normal.

After a month of being cared for at Deacon's Hospital, an acute care facility had to be found. Safe Care, that Sunny the visiting nurse had recommended was just one floor above the floor where Karen was staying. The admission process began and soon Karen was moved to Safe Care.

The big factors in Karen being admitted to Safe Care were her continued staph infection. It was by no means out of her body. Dr. Bronson had told us that staph could hide in the body for six or more months. Hopefully in a few months Karen could be weaned from the IV antibiotics and given oral medication. Another factor of course was the healing of the wound. How long the healing of this wound would take was questionable. Surgery was a possibility. But even with a surgical procedure the medical team was telling us that the time frame for healing of this wound would be many months and tedious care.

What a tragedy. Six months in a nursing home. Now, it appears it is going to take eight to twelve months to get over all the damage that was done: a wound the size of Mammoth Cave and a life threatening staph infection was more than enough; but further, a level of nutrition that only contributed to Karen's poor health; her sheer abuse by neglecting basic care of simply turning her to a different position several times a day; aides physically hurting her because they were too tired to move her properly, and so they basically yanked her from her chair to the bed. This doesn't include the violation of her rights by preventing her to leave the nursing home and the slander of my name by the administration saying that I was going to be involved in anything like an assisted suicide.

Here is a question. *Who needs it?*

You don't need the kind of garbage I just listed in the above paragraph or the many other infractions Karen suffered at the hands of Anglican River. You put your loved one in a nursing care facility to be cared for. You don't put them in to be starved, neglected, hurt and made worse than when they entered the facility. You put them in to be cared for.

Unfortunately, it is almost a given in our country that the nursing home is the last stop in life before death. This is why nursing homes get by with taking your thousands of dollars every month and allowing your loved one to get worse and worse until they die. We expect people to die in nursing homes. There is always someone waiting to take their place in their bed. This person, or usually our government will pay the thousands of dollars for the rent on the bed, and life in the nursing home industry goes on as usual—horrible.

When a good doctor and medical care facility comes along it makes any patient and his/her family want to stand on the kitchen table and shout that there is actually somebody and someplace in the medical society that cares and is willing to try to help.

22

A Little Prevention— Please!

One of the first moves that Deacon's Hospital made was to put Karen on an air flotation mattress. This mattress has a system that goes at the foot of the bed that may sit on the floor or attach to the end of the bed. This motorized equipment pushes air through a specially designed mattress. This mattress is especially formulated for people who spend most of their time in bed. It was created so that it would move or form to the body in such a way that bedsores (decubitus ulcers) might be prevented. While this special mattress is no guarantee against bedsores they are a tremendous help in preventing them.

Special cushions are also on the market for people who have to sit a lot. While there may be different types, Rolo is the type that Deacon's Hospital had for Karen when she had to be placed in her wheelchair.

When Karen was moved from Deacon's to Safe Care she was immediately placed on one of these air-supported mattresses. The facility also made sure Karen had the special cushion for when she was sitting in her wheelchair.

I have to ask the question, *why didn't Anglican River have Karen on this mattress?* They were dressing her wound every day and were very aware of Karen's increasing horrible situation.

With all the money that Medicare and Medicaid give to nursing home facilities, the least a nursing home could do, would be to provide these mattresses for patients like Karen to sleep on. The provision of such a mattress and cushion could have prevented Karen's wound and also could have prevented Karen from having a surgery that required her very tailbone be cut off to eliminate any signs of staph infection.

It is beyond any sensible sane thinking person why a nursing home facility would let bedfast patients sleep and rest on hard mattresses and sit on hard cushions when better equipment is available for their care.

The obvious reason is that corporations have one goal in mind and that's profit. Profit is a must if any business or organization is to do well. Unfortunately in this instance, people in nursing homes are hurt seriously by conditions that could be made better. All that is required is for the administration to order these special mattresses for the bedfast patients and the special cushion for when they are placed in their wheelchairs to sit for hours at a time. A few extra dollars have to be spent but lives are greatly spared so much physical torture. The country is also saved millions of dollars in the long run.

Sadly nursing home owners deposit large sums of cash into their own personal bank accounts, while someone's spouse, mother or father lies on a cheap hard mattress or sits on a chair that is only creating the potential for big time trouble—huge, ugly open wounds that have the potential for infection and death of the loved one.

Karen entered Deacon's Hospital on May 8. On June 27, a surgery was scheduled for Karen's wound. Over six weeks was spent by the medical staff of Deacon's Hospital and Safe Care trying to enhance the healing of the wound on it's own. While the wound did begin to heal— *very slowly*, the overseeing physicians felt Karen's only hope, with her tailbone showing the staph infection, was to remove the parts of the bone infected and then utilize some skin flaps taken from other parts of Karen's body to create flaps of skin that would cover the external open area of the wound. The tricky part was that the internal section of the wound would still be an open crevice and would still need many months of very special care in order to heal internally. This would mean of course that many months of making sure that Karen was not spending too much time seated or lying on her back side would have to be insured.

The very disease of multiple sclerosis is enough. Dealing with the daily struggles that come with the loss of one's body functions is bad enough. On top of this add a huge decubitus that requires special attention and care and it only adds to the problem.

Sickness of one kind brings another illness of another kind and they seem to mount up.

However, nursing home administrations such as Casey, Flossy and Roberta are supposedly trained people. They are working under the guise of being capable qualified people in their fields. They take large sums of money paid by government Medicare/Medicaid funds that are paid into by taxpayers. Why can't they make a simple move to help a debilitated nursing home resident out? The ordering of a special mattress would be so cost effective for our government.

If Casey, Flossy or Roberta or anyone involved in the nursing home administration or nursing leadership could stock a few decent mattresses and cushions for their patients, then the United States would be saved mega millions of dollars. Is this some crazy far-fetched analogy? No. Any nursing home could stock a dozen or so of these special mattresses and cushions and use them for their patients who need them. When one dies they move the mattress to another room. Not everyone in the nursing home is bedfast. People who are able to get up and walk around a little are not likely to develop the huge open wounds. A lot of people in the nursing homes are seen walking the building on walkers all the time. These people make it fine on normal mattresses. If these special mattresses were installed, then people like Karen would not likely develop the wound and then would not require three months of hospitalization in an acute care facility. How much do you think a mattress costs Medicare/Medicaid in comparison to three months in an acute care facility? I don't think it takes a rocket scientist to figure out that an ounce of prevention would be worth tons of cure. I'm talking about people's lives and families being spared enormous grief.

I'm talking about enormous sums of money that is drawn out of the taxpayers' pockets of America to cover these kinds of medical costs that are created by a bunch of nursing home administrators who are paid a few extra dollars by their corporation to balance a budget. The federal government could save us all a lot of money and people a lot of grief by demanding safer medical care of our loved ones.

What does the federal government have to do with it? Our nation is paying for the bulk of nursing home care in our country. Average citizens cannot afford the multi thousands of dollars that it costs each month to have a loved one as a nursing home resident. State health department officials who are state and federally funded need to step in and save some lives, grief and our nation further financial stress.

23

Nursing Home Abuse And Neglect

The anticipated surgery that took place at Deacon's Hospital would be the culmination of the horrifying care received at Anglican River. What was supposed to be six months of care now had resulted in many additional weeks of recuperation, surgery, tailbone loss and many more additional weeks of further recuperation in an acute care facility. The uncomfortable misery of overcoming a surgery would be one more thing that Karen would have to emotionally and mentally endure. Her large open pressure sore was a very public demonstration of nursing home neglect.

The many months of Karen lying in bed with a fever and no one in the nursing home trying to find out was a major neglect by the physicians, administration and nurses.

The continuation of using a standard mattress and cushion was a daily neglect of the nursing home.

Allowing a tiny red spot to grow and grow and grow until it became an open pressure sore and then allowing it to become the size of a baseball is just incredulous . . . or rather obscene.

The daily neglect of not providing adequate meals is another major issue. The nursing home administration and nurse Flossy should have had enough education to know Karen was losing her essential proteins and calories through her open wound. Foods and supplements were vitally essential to combat this nutritional loss. All kinds of delicious protein bars and drinks are available today. It is only a lack of interest or concern by the nursing home leadership that would even permit a patient to die a little every day by not providing the proper nutrition.

Horrible hygiene is another deploring factor. Three baths a week is what nursing home patients receive in most cases. No wonder the places in so many cases smell so bad. We are talking about patients who have serious urinary problems. Leaky bladders and urinary problems are a rampant problem of aging. And yet the nursing home thinks they can get by with giving a patient three baths a week? In Karen's case having a catheter helped . . . but what about the bowel movements that I constantly found her lying in?

Administrator Casey told me, "Glenn, whenever you find your wife that way tell a nurse or an aide and we'll clean it up." I understand that an aide cannot be right on the spot twenty-four hours a day to catch every bowel movement within a minute of it occurring. However, I am talking about finding Karen in bowel movements so old they had dried to her skin.

It was common for me to pick Karen up out of bed and place her in her wheelchair and between the three feet of distance between the bed and chair have dried feces fall on the floor. I would go to the bathroom and get tissue to clean up the mess. I probably should have called an aide but I knew these poor women were already strained to the hilt and so that's why I went ahead and cleaned it up. Plus, I love Karen and love encompasses a lot.

One morning all this dried feces fell out of Karen's bed when I was transporting her to her chair and I decided to let it lie on the floor. I wanted the aides or nursing staff to clean it up. I really felt disgusted seeing this pile of feces on the floor of my wife's room. It was dry so it wasn't messy nor really smelled that bad. Likely the feces were already more than a day old and had stayed attached to Karen's behind until I moved her.

I never mentioned it to Karen because I knew she would be embarrassed about the bowel movement. Nor would she want something like this being on the floor of her room in broad open sight of anyone who came into the room. Yet with Karen in her chair and titled backward a little so she could look up and watch television I knew she would likely never notice the feces on the floor.

I came back to the nursing home that evening—over ten hours later and the feces was still in the floor . . . unmoved or untouched. I was in shock. No nurse or aide had bothered to move it.

I came back the next morning and the feces were still on the floor. I couldn't believe that an aide or somebody would not bother to dispose of it. I came back that evening and low and behold it had finally disappeared. Sometime during the day house keeping likely came in to sweep and probably cleaned up the mess. I feel assured that the feces were allowed to lay on Karen's floor for more than twenty-four hours. If aides and nurses are so overworked that they don't have the time to pick such a mess up off the floor or don't care about doing it, then something is very wrong. And, that is the whole problem with our American nursing home industry. Something is very wrong and there are a lot of disgraces to our loved one that are occurring. These are disgraces that are against them and our society.

The very sheer lack of medical care is another startling injustice that was dished out by Anglican River. Is it this way in every nursing home? I do not in any way want to discredit Dr. Youngblood who was away on medical leave. Yet, I feel it was the place of Anglican River to provide doctors to oversee their patients. A monthly visit from a physician as provided by most nursing homes may in many cases be sufficient. But, two doctor's visits in six months, (as Karen received) is not enough medical attention for a nursing home resident especially one that is fighting fever day and night.

There are many other sad instances that occurred at Anglican River. Sadly, most all of them could have been prevented but weren't. Sadly, they continue at this very moment. Who do you have at Anglican River that is lying in a fever with an infection that is about to take his or her life? Who do you have there lying in a bowel movement? Who do you have at Anglican River that needs turning in bed? They have had their call light on all night but no one has come to help them. They are there defenseless, helpless and very alone. Their condition is worsening because a doctor has not seen them. The doctor is supposed to check on them once a month. Will the doctor really see them this month? Can your loved one really make it the entire month until the doctor comes? And when the doctor visits your loved one and has 139 more patients in the facility to see . . . just how much attention and examination do you think your loved will receive? Think about it!

As Americans we have allowed a monster to be created. This monster has almost card blanc freedom to roam freely, grow and flex its muscles as it consumes helpless lives and devours billions of dollars from the national treasury.

Periodically, State Health Departments issue little citations or slap a nursing home on the back of the hand for a reported incident. Occasionally, there is a report of a nursing home license being pulled; but licenses are reinstated as soon as the incident is changed or the situation satisfactorily fixed. Nursing home administrators and owners smile their little smiles whenever an infraction about them is reported. They know they are moving ahead full throttle with their daily jobs and activities and nothing is going to shut them down. They will appease the state officials and then resume doing whatever they want to do and to whomever they choose to do it to.

However, nursing homes and their corporations don't like to be sued. It's unfortunate, but sometimes you have to get an attorney and the law involved. When your loved one is abused, then the loved one and family have every right for legal recourse. What other leverage do you have for your protection? If you ignore this right of legal recourse then our nursing home industry can kill and bury our loved ones whenever they get tired of seeing their call lights or whenever they get tired of listening to your loved one cry for help. And believe me, scores of people in nursing homes in America every day are crying for someone to help them to the bathroom, bring them some water or just help them turn over in bed. The fact that nursing homes take the billions of dollars they make from American tax-payers and pay in most cases, big administrative salaries and do not hire adequate help to care for people is no excuse for the neglect and even severe abuse of these many elderly or disabled loved ones.

24

Removing Karen's Tailbone

Physicians who attended to Karen during her stay at Deacon's Hospital and then Safe Care determined the only way to enhance healing of Karen's pressure sore was through extensive surgery.

The surgery took place on June 27.

Karen and I had our prayer time together at 11:00 a.m. At 11:30 I was kissing her goodbye as the nurses were wheeling her into the surgery room. I would wait in surgery waiting for four hours. At 3:30 the surgeon came out to explain to me what he had done.

He felt like the surgery had gone as planned.

He had literally cut out the sore. He had to remove about one inch of the very bottom of Karen's tailbone. It was the only way the staph infection, which had permanently got into this section of the bone, could be removed.

It was horrifying as he told about literally having to use a saw and chisel to remove the bone.

Flaps of skin were then taken from sections around Karen's backside to cover the opening. Tubes were left inside the sore so that the infection could run out for the next several days.

Karen would be placed on an even more specialized mattress than what she had been sleeping on. The mattress would permit her to lie on her backside without applying any pressure to the surgically treated wound.

The healing process could still take a couple of months and even longer. The bedsore from the external view would soon look covered and healed. Internally would be another story. The large internal cavern would require weeks for healing which meant much serious care in protecting the treated area. For weeks Karen would be turned every two hours and kept in a position that would allow the sore to internally heal.

Once Karen is at home or any other kind of facility, extreme care will need to be performed to insure that the external skin does not break down. The thought of the external portion of the skin breaking down and opening to expose an underlying cavern that may not have completely healed is unnerving.

Karen would be required to stay in a specialized bed for over four weeks before being allowed to sit up in a chair of any kind. This very painful extensive surgical operation was the culminating reward of Karen's six-month stay at Anglican River Nursing Home.

25

Nightmare Stories From Around The Country

Nursing home abuse can happen in many ways. This may or may not include both physical and emotional abuse or neglect. Here are some signs to watch for:

Emotional Abuse
   Upset or agitated
   Non-communicative or withdrawn
   Behavior such as biting, rocking or sucking

Physical Abuse
   Wounds that are open, cuts, bruises, welts or discolorations
   Caregiver cannot explain adequately the condition
   Weight loss
   Burns from acids, caustics or cigarettes

Neglect
   Begs for food
   Dehydration, malnutrition, pressure sores
   Unsanitary and unclean conditions
   Dirt, soiled bed, fecal or urine odor

From Illinois comes the story of one nightmarish nursing home incident. A daughter told me the story of what happened to her mother.

"Mom was in her eighties and was in a room by herself. She couldn't talk very loud. Actually, her voice volume was just a whisper. She was very coherent but vocally we had to listen carefully to understand her. An aide raped her one night. In the middle of the night, a large man who worked as an aide for the nursing home came in and raped her. There was nothing that she could do about it. He was a big man and my mother couldn't scream for help. She didn't have a roommate that could help her. My sister who lived nearby had suspected things weren't going right in this nursing home for several weeks and came in at five in the morning to check on mom and found a couple of other aides had our mother completely naked in bed throwing away the clothing that mom had been wearing. Those aides never let on what had just happened to my poor mother. Mom told my sister, and then all of us, how this man came into her room in the middle of the night and raped her."

She continued, "We tried to have that man put behind bars but nothing ever became of him. The judge threw our case out of court. Several months later we found out the judge had even hired this guy to work for him. However, we did shut the nursing home down. It doesn't exist anymore. Mom died shortly after that horrible incident. She became so depressed and withdrawn that I think she gave up."

This case alone is cause for anyone to want a roommate in a nursing home. In Karen's case, Luella came to Karen's rescue on many occasions. Karen's voice, too, was very un-audible. For months it was nothing more than a whisper because of the respirator she had been on for so long in the hospital.

There were many nights she laid with fever and was unable to help herself. Luella was always helping Karen to call or search for an aide or nurse to help her. Without a roommate, nursing home residents are left to almost any unscrupulous or abusive treatment.

From Indiana a case is in progress of one nursing home resident that came into the room of another resident at night and smothered her to death. The attacker was a mental case who was supposed to be kept under 24 hour scrutiny, but an aide says he often wondered out of his room and later would be found at some other part of the building wandering the hall. One night he wandered out once too many and took another resident's life.

During Karen's stay at Anglican River, one lady constantly wandered into her and Luella's room . . . got in their closet . . . went through their dresser and was always trying to get into bed with one of them. Luella would tell me on several occasions how scared she was of the woman. Aides and nurses would laugh about the woman, as they would chase her back into her room. But who wants to wake up at two in the morning and have another resident standing over your bed peering into your face? Or who wants to awaken in the night and hear an intruder going through your closet? Karen and Luella said, "It's very scary."

TIME Magazine, August 3, 1998
"Shining a Light on Abuse"
Mark Thompson
© 1998 Time Inc. reprinted by permission

> Leslie Oliva watched her mother move through three California nursing homes during the last three years of her life. "My mother experienced beating, malnutrition, dehydration and neglect," Oliva said quietly. "All three of the nursing homes are responsible for her death."
> In a written statement provided to the Senate Special Committee on Aging, Oliva says her mother Marie Espinoza, who was suffering from a degenerative brain disease, had bruises, bedsores and a broken pelvis within months after her 1985 arrival at the Orangetree Convalescent Hospital. Food was often left at the foot of

the bed, out of her reach. She began to lose weight. "She always seemed to be starving or begging for water," says Oliva in her official account. At Extended Care Hospital, Espinoza suffered severe dehydration and bedsores. Last January she entered Palm Terrace Convalescent Center. The nursing home said she died after choking on food, but Oliva plans to tell the committee that this makes no sense. Espinoza was supposed to be fed through a tube. All three nursing homes deny any wrongdoing.

Oliva's tale will put a human face on a damning study by the General Accounting Office that will be the subject of hearings by the Committee on Aging this week. The panel has summoned two insiders—a former California nursing home nurse and a current nursing home inspector for the state to offer firsthand accounts of the horrors. The women—called "Clara B" and "Florence N" by the committee—will speak from behind a screen to shield them from retaliation by the powerful nursing home industry and the agency that provides care to California's elderly.

"If they didn't eat fast enough, the food got taken away from them," the former nursing home employee told Time. She says she would falsify records to show that the residents had eaten everything on their plate. Things would improve for a while when state inspectors showed up for their predictably timed annual visit. "The attitude was to put a Band-Aid on it until the state left, and then it'd go right back to the way it was," she says. The inspector, who has been visiting California nursing homes for years told Time her complaints are regularly ignored because of the "cronyism" that exists between the state overseers and nursing home operators. "Once we write down violations, the nursing homes dismiss our citations," she says. This has led to "hopelessness" among inspectors like herself she says.

And, according the GAO, it has contributed to the litany of abuses. One resident lost a third of his body weight over seven weeks. During this time, the nursing home failed to weigh him, give him prescribed painkillers or alert his doctor to his worsening condition. Another resident had a bedsore, and the doctor ordered the bandage to be changed twice a day; it was unchanged for nearly two weeks. A third nursing home resident was brought to a hospital, where the patient was found to have had a broken leg for at least three weeks and the nursing home records were missing. A woman whose four bedsores were exposed to the bone and required daily cleaning was rarely given the prescribed pain medicine before the procedure.

The GAO report, following up on a story that appeared in Time last fall, says more than half the suspicious deaths studied in California nursing homes were probably due to neglect, including malnutrition and dehydration. The study says that nearly 1 in 3 California nursing homes has been cited by state inspectors for "serious or potentially life threatening care problems" and that the same problems probably exist across the nation. These are likely to grow as baby boomers become grandparents and the rocketing elderly population puts even greater pressure on the nation's nursing homes. Senator Charles Grassley argued that much of the blame for the flawed nursing home system can be pinned on the Federal Government, which has the economic leverage to insist on improvements. Last year the Federal Government spent $28 billion on nursing home care through Medicare and Medicaid. "It's been too permissive and too forgiving in its enforcement," Grassley told Time.

In the face of such stinging criticism, President Clinton announced that his administration was cracking down on abuses in the 17,000 nursing homes across the nation that house 1.6 million of the old and disabled. "We are failing our parents, and we must do more," Clinton said. The President said repeat nursing home violators need to be fined quickly and stopped from avoiding payment by pledging to fix the problem. He urged states to stop conducting nursing home inspections during business hours at precise one-year intervals "so there is no time to hide neglect and abuse." And he wants more nursing home workers trained to give residents food and water.

The GAO further reported that many nursing homes have become dangerous places largely because they are understaffed—and under regulated. Nursing homes spend 2 out of every three dollars on payroll, so the most tempting way for them to increase profits is to cut personnel. And the

Federal Government isn't halting this practice, says GAO. The "forgiving enforcement stance" of the Health Care Financing Administration "helps explain how some homes can repeatedly harm residents without facing sanctions."

Time reported last fall on a study by Palo Alto, California attorney Von Packard and investigators Robert Bauman and Dina Rasor of the death certificates of all Californians who died in nursing homes from 1986 through 1993. In more than 7% of the cases, lack of food or water, untreated bedsores or infections were listed as a cause of death. This probe led Grassley to order the GAO to California to investigate. The GAO's medical review of 62 residents who died in trouble-prone California nursing homes showed that 34 of them received poor care that probably contributed to their demise. Applying the GAO's percentage of negligent California deaths to the nation's nursing home population suggests that close to 20,000 U.S. nursing home residents are dying prematurely or in unnecessary pain, or both.

"Everyone knows that profits and good care are not compatible" is how Pat McGinnis, executive director of California Advocates for Nursing Home Reform, explains the persistence of nursing home abuses. But a recent spate of multimillion-dollar jury awards to nursing home residents and their families because of poor care may force some homes to improve. A California woman won a $95 million verdict after the jury was told how she broke her shoulder and shattered her hip (the award was cut to $3 million), and a jury awarded $6.3 million to the family of a Florida man who wandered from his nursing home and drowned in a pond.

While regulators are supposed to ensure that standards are met, many of the rules are weak or unclear. The Federal Government, for example, doesn't specify how much staffing a nursing home needs. That imprecision and split responsibility can be exploited by the nursing home industry, which in many states is a powerful lobby with lots of cash to spread among sympathetic lawmakers. Last year California levied $2.6 million in fines, but it has collected only $518,000 from recalcitrant nursing homes.

Evidence like the GAO report is sure to encourage even more lawyers to file suits seeking damages for alleged wrongdoing by nursing homes.

Highlights from the GAO Report

- Deadly Care . . . Detailed medical reviews of 62 California deaths in which negligence was suspected turned up evidence that 34 of those deaths—55% were probably caused by poor care.

- Poor Grades . . . Only 30 of California's 1,370 nursing homes passed state inspections in the past three years with minimal or no problems; 407 were cited for care that "caused death or serious harm."

- Bad Oversight . . . Nursing homes temporarily beef up staff and often falsify records to fool inspectors, and "can mask significant care problems from the view of federal and state regulators."

TIME Magazine, October 27, 1997
"Fatal Neglect"
Mark Thompson
© 1997 Time Inc. reprinted by permission

In possibly thousands of cases, nursing home residents are dying from a lack of food and water and the most basic level of hygiene.

Once she moved into Creekside Care Convalescent Hospital, it didn't take Bessie Seday long to realize that the promises made to her by the nursing home before she had arrived had evaporated. "I couldn't get anybody's attention, starting on the fourth day," recalls the bed bound 84 year old. "You'd have your call light on for hours, but nobody came." What made her waiting more desolate was the near total deprivation of sunlight during her four months at Creekside. "It was a dungeon," she says. "I really would have liked to see the sunshine, but they never put us outside." Things only got worse when the sun set, and the staff ignored calls for help or painkillers. "The screaming is what got me the worst, the screaming when the lights went out," she says. "I couldn't fall asleep until 1 or 2 in the morning with all that screaming going on."

Bessie's daughter Ann used to visit her mother in the home, some 50 miles northeast of San Francisco, and find her lying immobile in a filthy bed. "She was not turned and kept clean and dry, which led to the bedsores," Ann recalls. A bedsore on Bessie's left hip turned into a gaping wound that would not heal, despite repeated whirlpool baths. Creekside nurse Patricia Lloyd knew why: the special washing machine for cleaning dirty bedpans had broken down. "So we washed bedpans in the whirlpool," she says, "and then we'd put patients with big bedsores, like Bessie Seday, in there." Fixing Bessie's wound required repeated surgery, including the removal of her left buttock and part of her pelvis. "They were washing her," says Lesley Clement, her attorney, "in a cesspool."

Bessie, who now lives with her daughter, was lucky to get out alive. A Time investigation has found that senior citizens in nursing homes are at far greater risk of death from neglect than their loved ones imagine. Owing to the work of lawyers, investigators and politicians who have begun examining the causes of thousands of nursing home deaths across the U.S., the grim details are emerging of an extensive blood-chilling and for-profit pattern of neglect. In Chicago last week a 73 count indictment was returned against a hospice operator charged with bilking Medicare and others of $28 million for services to the terminally ill that were never delivered. In Detroit a nursing home that was part of a chain whose owner was convicted of Medicaid fraud 17 years ago was cited again last year for bad hygiene, inattention to frail residents and incompetent staff. In Texas, attorney general Dan Morales filed 50 lawsuits against nursing homes this year for neglect and failure to medicate.

Neglectful caregivers are preying not only on elderly residents but also on American taxpayers. More than $45 billion in government funds, mostly from Medicare and Medicaid, is pumped into nursing homes annually, an amount that comes to nearly 60% of the national tab for such eldercare. In order to pocket a larger slice of the federal stipend, many nursing homes—largely for profit enterprises—provide a minimal level of care, if that.

Death comes to the elderly in many ways, including heart and lung failure, chronic disease and plain bad luck. But David Hoffman, an assistant U.S. attorney in Philadelphia, though he spied something else at work last year, when he saw festering bedsores eating away the flesh of three residents in a local nursing home. He knew the home had been pocketing government money the residents were given to ensure good care, and he saw the bedsores as proof that they weren't getting it. He investigated and later sued Geriatric and Medical Companies Inc., which operated the Tucker House nursing home. The nursing home company settled the case for $600,000, sent condolences to the families of the three residents and perhaps most important—set off probes by law firms around the country seeking similar evidence of poor care and the resulting fraud.

The idea of using death certificates to try to prove fraud was born at the Creekside facility. Shortly after Rhoda

Johnson moved into room 52 of the nursing home in 1992, her daughter Ila Swan became concerned about her care. Swan, a 57 year old former telephone worker, says her anxiety grew when she saw a woman in room 51, across the hall, try to climb out of bed after her calls for a nurse went unanswered for an hour. According to the woman's roommate, as the woman struggled to get out of the bed, she toppled and struck her head on the tile floor. She lay there for 20 minutes, her cries for help going unanswered by the staff as a pool of blood grew around her. She died a short time later. Swan visited the country records office to review the woman's death certificate and those of others who had died while residing at Creekside and other nearby nursing homes. She was startled to find 10 questionable causes of death listed on the first 30 she reviewed. "They'd listed malnutrition, dehydration, bedsores and urinary tract infections as causes of death," Swan says. "These nursing homes were killing people."

Soon Rasor and investigator Robert Bauman heard of Swan's work. Intrigued, they began working with Packard to obtain records listing the cause and place of death for every one in California who died from 1986 to 1993. More than 300,000 had died in nursing homes.

What happened next surprised Rasor and Bauman most. Nearly 22,000 of the nursing home deaths were attributed to lack of food or water, infections or internal obstructions—all preventable, at least in theory. Packard and his investigators didn't add deaths to their list if the deceased suffered from other ailments that exacerbated those four causes. So people who died of both cancer and malnutrition, for example, were not counted.

Generally, the nursing home industry likes to settle lawsuits quietly and often hands over money only in exchange for silence. But that didn't happen at Creekside, where lawsuits alleging neglect have recently been getting into the public record. Four former residents of Creekside have won more than $2 million in settlements after alleging poor care. An additional four suits are pending. In fact, Packard's California death list contains the names of dozens of people who died there.

Creekside, which opened in 1989, is a handsome place, its fieldstone walled foyer graced by a big aquarium. Its brochure boasted of private patios and a recreation director who "understands the subtle limitations of age." It promised "all the comforts of home" plus "state of the art nursing equipment" for its 120 residents.

Court records and interviews tell a different story. "The whole place was a fiasco," says nurse Patricia Lloyd, who moved away from California after she testified against Creekside, where she worked for four years, until 1995. "Everybody was sick; everybody was having problems." Did such care lead to premature deaths among Creekside residents? "Absolutely," Lloyd says firmly and quickly. "I'm 100% sure. People would come in, they'd get depressed, stop eating and start falling. Then they'd get tied down to a chair, and they'd rapidly decline and die. That was something that was pretty common at Creekside."

Feeding was always a problem, says Suzanne Cologgi, a former Creekside nurse's aide. "The staff would give up really quickly, so the patient wouldn't get enough food," Cologgi says. "Because there wasn't enough staff, a lot of people went without eating or sat in dirty diapers." Many times Cologgi would have 20 minutes to feed seven residents, all of whom depended on her to spoon every bit of food into their mouth. "Sometimes you would need 30 minutes for one," she recalls. "Full trays would go back untouched."

Patients who ate poorly were supposed to get 240 calorie liquid supplements to help them gain weight. "We didn't even pass them out, even though we signed forms indicating that they got them," Lloyd says. "Sometimes, patients who could talk would ask for them, and get them, but the patients who couldn't talk didn't—and they were the ones who really needed them." Medical charts, Lloyd says, were routinely falsified.

Rhoda Johnson, Ila Swan's mother, lived at Creekside nearly two years, until July 1993. Her family alleged in a lawsuit that the nursing home essentially abandoned Johnson: she was often left lying in her own waste, hungry cold, unfed and unturned. One day she complained to Swan that her hip hurt. With her sons' help, Swan lifted her mother out of the bed, pulled up her nightgown and collapsed in sobs. "She had this bedsore on her hip that was so deep," her daughter recalls, "that I could see the hip socket and leg bone moving inside." Her bottom was bruised and caked with dried feces, which Swan peeled off with her fingers amid her tears. "I never had looked under the covers," she says. "I didn't think I had to." Johnson, now 98 and living in a Utah nursing home, doesn't' talk much about her experience. "Creekside was mean to me," she says. "They didn't give me a drink, they yelled at me, they hurt me." She received a $775,000 settlement in May 1996.

In the past year nearly 10,000 of the 15,000 nursing homes inspected by the states had violations, and many were forwarded to federal officials with proposed punishments. But fines or other penalties were imposed in only 2% of the cases. State inspectors recommended to U.S. authorities that 5,458 nursing homes—1 in every three—be barred from collecting money for new patients. Washington cut that figure to 156. The states urged Washington to order special training for the staff in 3,039 nursing homes; Washington ordered such training for only 103. And state inspectors urged Washington to fine 2,935 nursing homes for violations. The Federal Government fined only 228 (and those that paid without appealing had to pay only 65% of the fine).

And then there are the maggots. In 1994 a nurse at the Fairfield Health Care Center in Fairfield, California found about 40 maggots in a bedsore on the left heel of an 87-year-old man. State inspectors recommended a $24,000 fine, but the nursing home appealed, saying the wriggling larvae didn't constitute evidence of poor care. Besides, the nursing home argued, maggots are good for eating away dead tissue inside a wound. The state hearing officer agreed with the nursing home and threw out the fine.

Brenda Klutz, deputy director of licensing for California's health department, calls that decision "very distressing and emotional," but she doesn't call it wrong. In fact, she echoes the nursing home's argument. "In an era of alternative medicine, maggots are being used for debridement of dead tissue," she says. "The fact that these

sorts of eggs and maggots can hatch in a 24-hour period may not even mean that there was improper wound care." With regulators like that, the elderly in nursing homes may have more to fear than either the maggots or the nursing home operators."
—With reporting by James L. Graff/Chicago and S.C. Gwynne/Austin

Making the decision to move a parent/spouse into a nursing home is painful. Emotionally it was the toughest decision I've ever made and unfortunately I regret Karen's six-month experience at Anglican River.

If you have to begin looking for a nursing home then consult with the state's survey of inspections. Each state conducts inspections about once a year and issues a survey of its findings that should be available at all nursing homes. Even a good nursing home may be cited for deficiencies, but they should be minor and promptly fixed. Bad signs: problems affecting resident's health, or an inability to produce the most recent surveys.

Federal law requires each state to have an ombudsman's office with information on all nursing homes. To contact your ombudsman, call the National Citizens' Coalition for Nursing Homes Reform in Washington at (202) 332-2275.

Make an unannounced visit to prospective nursing homes. Look, listen and smell. Wander hallways, speak to residents and staff; get a sense if both enjoy being there. A nursing home that won't let you visit unannounced may well have something to hide. Look for clean, well-groomed residents. Discreetly try to assess oral hygiene. Listen for staff's tone in dealing with residents. Make sure that nurses and aides mingle with residents and don't view their changes as widgets on an assembly line. While most nursing homes occasionally smell of urine and feces, there should be no persistent stench or overwhelming scent of air fresheners.

Keep your eyes open. Watch the call lights that residents use to summon help. See how long it takes for help to arrive—more than five minutes is too long. Look for obstacles or puddles left in corridors that could endanger frail residents with failing vision. Visit during a meal: assess the food, and check that those who can't feed themselves are helped. Keep your eyes peeled for residents in restraints; the more you see the more leery you should be.

Once you've picked a home, visit frequently. Residents in nursing homes that are abandoned by family are not going to receive the same treatment as residents who have family going daily to check on them.

Author's Note

Why are there so few books like this one on Nursing Homes in America? Because the people in nursing homes seldom live to write a book. They are often elderly people and the nursing home is their last stop before death. By the time they become residents in a nursing home they often don't have the physical or mental fortitude to write their story. Henceforth, thousands of nursing homes get by with neglecting and even abusing people in the final stage of life when help and care is most needed. Dead people can't tell their story. It is uncommon that young adult families such as Karen and I would experience nursing home life. If our experience was horrible, it is terrifying to think about what elderly Americans are enduring. They are most likely living life's final nightmare.

Also by Dr. Glenn Mollette

Silent Struggler
A Caregiver's Personal Story

    This book is the personal story of Glenn Mollette and his role as caregiver to his wife, Karen. It deals with almost every issue faced by the caregiver. This is a must book for every family or person experiencing chronic illness in a care-giving role.

ISBN 0-9704650-0-9   Published by Inspiration

Spiritual Chocolate

    Spiritual Chocolate is about the good, sweet and delightful life that God has for us in Christ. While much of life has its valleys and trials, God provides a newness of life that nothing in the world can give to us. This life is one of hope, power, stamina, peace and the ability to soar even when life's conditions seem unfavorable for flying. The very best treasures in life come directly from the heart of God. He loves us. This chocolate is good for you!

ISBN 0-9704650-2-5   Published by Inspiration

These books may be ordered through your local bookstore or BarnesandNoble.com, BooksaMillion.com or Amazon.com.

Please check out:

Fixing Frannie

by Frannie Rose

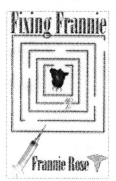

This is a heart-warming, humorous and inspirational story of Frannie Rose. Her story is one of sheer courage and determination as she weaves her way through a very frustrating medical maze to recover her health. Anyone who has ever been sick and has been through countless tests, doctor's appointments and multiple treatments to no avail may see themselves in many instances through the eyes of Frannie Rose.

ISBN 0-9704650-1-7
Publisher: GMA Publishing

Available through your local bookstore or BarnesandNoble.com,
BooksaMillion.com or Amazon.com.

10443732

CPSIA information can be obtained at www.ICGtesting.com
Printed in the USA
LVOW12s2000241013

358461LV00001B/327/A